INSIGHT INTO

DEMENTIA

INSIGHT INTO

DEMENTIA

Rosemary Hurtley

Foreword by Dr Daphne Wallace

CWR

Published 2010 by CWR, Waverley Abbey House, Waverley Lane, Farnham, Surrey GU9 8EP
England. CWR is a Registered Charity – Number 294387 and a Limited Company registered in
England – Registration Number 1990308.

See back of book for list of National Distributors.

Whilst every effort has been made to source all references, we acknowledge that some may be
incomplete.
Poems by Patricia Duff on pages 39, 51 are used by permission.
The poem by Edith Brooking on page 104 is used by permission.

Unless otherwise indicated, all Scripture references are from the Holy Bible: New International
Version (NIV), copyright © 1973, 1978, 1984 by the International Bible Society.
Concept development, editing, design and production by CWR

Printed in China by 1010 Printing International Ltd.

ISBN: 978-1-85345-561-2

Rosemary has described dementia and its effects in an accessible way. Her insights enable you to see the person and not the dementia. By including scriptures throughout the book she has connected the relationship and hope that stems from faith in God and coping with a debilitating illness.

Sharon Blackburn RGN RMN

Written with insight and compassion, including carefully chosen Bible readings and prayers to give comfort and strength, this is an invaluable guide by someone who really understands because she has been there herself. It would have been wonderful to have had this resource when I really needed it.

Joanna Howse, carer of a husband with dementia

From a wealth of both personal and professional experience Rosemary Hurtley has written clearly and succinctly. It is only too easy to discuss dementia care with bias and emotive comment, bringing feelings of guilty obligation. This book, on the other hand, will leave its readers accurately informed, empowered, and greatly encouraged.

Marion Osgood, writer, and Hugh Osgood, international Bible teacher

I found this to be a practical, informative text reflecting contemporary knowledge and approaches to dementia care. It distinguishes itself from the many other books about dementia currently available by its Christian spiritual context.

Clive Evers, Alzheimer's Society

This is a much needed resource with all the things you need to know about how dementia impacts on a person and ways to support them.

Claire Craig, Occupational Therapist

WAVERLEY ABBEY INSIGHT SERIES

The Waverley Abbey Insight Series has been developed in response to the great need to help people understand and face some key issues that many of us struggle with today. CWR's ministry spans teaching, training and publishing, and this series draws on all of these areas of ministry.

Sourced from material first presented on Insight Days by CWR at their base, Waverley Abbey House, presenters and authors have worked in close co-operation to bring this series together, offering clear insight, teaching and help on a broad range of subjects and issues. Bringing biblical understanding and godly insight, these books are written both for those who help others and those who face these issues themselves.

CONTENTS

Foreword written by Dr Daphne Wallace   8

Introduction   10

1. What is dementia?   13

2. The journey   27

3. Dementia care 1: Treatment   41

4. Dementia care 2: Wellbeing   53

5. Who is there to help?   67

6. Care options   81

7. Spiritual care   97

Resources   107

Appendix 1: Scriptures   112

Appendix 2: Restor8 Principles   117

Appendix 3: Relationship-centred care   119

Appendix 4: PAL   121

Notes   122

FOREWORD

Although general awareness and understanding of dementia has improved there is still a long way to go before we achieve anything like that achieved in the last fifty years for cancer. In the year since publication of the National Dementia Strategy for England it is increasingly evident that we have much misunderstanding and 'dis-information' to counter.

I welcome this book. Many carers with a Christian faith struggle to understand the pain and distress that can go with dementia in the context of their faith in a loving God. This book should go a long way towards helping them grapple with such difficulties. The provision of suggested activities, reflection and prayer at the end of each chapter helps greatly to aid reflection, particularly in a person-centred way and leads to meditative prayer. The use of poetry and biblical references assists the prayerful examination of the issues and our understanding and acceptance of them. The quotes at the head of each chapter are also helpful and thought provoking.

The first chapter gives a clear outline of the current knowledge of dementia in its different forms, and the impact of the illness on the person with dementia and their family and carers. One helpful aspect of this chapter is that it makes clear that dementia is not a unitary disease and, though Alzheimer's disease is the most common form, other pathologies are not uncommon and may present different problems. The second chapter looks at the journey to be travelled by the person with dementia and their family. In outlining current understanding of memory and other changes with normal ageing it also describes the process of diagnosis. The sections on the experience of dementia are informative and should help carers to a greater appreciation of the impact of the diagnosis.

Aspects of treatment and the need for a positive message to counter the old idea that 'nothing can be done' are outlined. A discussion of wellbeing and avoidance of ill-being are well explored, again with helpful examples and vignettes. The need for help and support, particularly for carers, is tackled with an outline of the various experts who should be there to help. With increasing pressure for more choices and care options it is helpful to have the outline of issues to be considered, especially in the later stages of the illness.

Much that is involved in spiritual care runs like a thread throughout the book but in the last chapter the specific issues involved in helping the person with dementia to maintain their spiritual life are thoughtfully explored, as is the need to recognise this in the context of care homes, which is welcome.

The last, very helpful, part of the book provides sources of further information and material, and elaborates on some of the systems and methods referred to in the text.

Overall this book is a welcome addition to the current literature on dementia and particularly useful to members of the Christian community.

Dr Daphne Wallace
Retired psychiatrist and person with dementia

INTRODUCTION

Dementia isn't when you can't find your car keys; it's when you're standing at the door and you don't know what they're there for.[1]

In Proverbs 23:33, we read: 'Your eyes will see strange sights and your mind will imagine confusing things' – this could be a description of living with dementia. Dementia! The very word seems to conjure up anxieties about being out of control of one's life, or images of a prolonged death sentence. There is so much fear, stigma and ignorance attached to it; as indeed there is with the ageing process itself. But we cannot choose to ignore dementia. We may have a loved one who has been diagnosed with it. We may have a friend who has a partner or parent suffering from the effects of it. In one way or another, many of our lives have been, or are, touched by it.

In this book, we will be taking a look at what it means to have dementia; what it is, the journey onwards from the initial diagnosis, dementia care, help and options and, of course, spiritual care. We will be exploring dementia and what it feels like, its impact; we will also see how as a church community we need to understand it, deciding strategies to include and show unconditional love to people with dementia, and their families.

Issues of care are crucial to address; it is important that quality services can be provided for our ageing population and, of course, we need to engage older people in what this whole package will look like. Because of the changes in society's attitudes and social engagement, use of technology and new health sciences, we will need imagination to find new ways of delivering care.

It's my hope that you will find this book informative, helpful and encouraging; that if you are walking down the dark path of this illness yourself, or accompanying a loved one, you might find within these pages the strength, hope and assistance you need for the journey.

Rosemary Hurtley
January 2010

CHAPTER ONE

WHAT IS DEMENTIA?

'Rise in the presence of the aged, show respect for the elderly
and revere your God.' (Leviticus 19:32)
'... do not despise your mother when she is old.'
(Proverbs 23:22)

INTRODUCTION

Our population is an ageing population. More than 13 million people in the UK will be over sixty-five by 2031. Most of those will be over eighty-five, with women outnumbering men.[1] Will this fact make age discrimination more or less of an issue? With such a diverse population, it may not be viable to still discuss older people as a group, and many will continue to work past retirement age. However, as the population ages, more people will need care and support – 50 per cent of those over seventy-five will have life-limiting illnesses, and dementia will affect one in four over the age of eighty-five.

But what *is* dementia?

In this chapter, we will examine what 'dementia' actually is, as well as thinking about age in general. Let's look at some facts and truths about ageing.

SOME FACTS ABOUT AGEING

- Ageing is not a disease, but part of the normal life process.
- Everyone ages differently; we become more diverse with age. Our bodies and minds become less efficient but we are still able to improve and develop, with active training.
- The process affects our physical, psychological, personality and cognitive aspects.
- Main contributors to dependency are a lack of mobility, poor mental health and cognitive problems.
- Successful ageing and quality of life is closely linked to maintaining and developing relationships, retaining contact with society, and having opportunities to develop, improve, maintain function and learn new things.
- Ageism and attitudes which stereotype older people frequently influence expectations, practice and outcomes, and need challenging. Western society holds in high esteem the values of beauty and eternal youth rather than the intrinsic value of all ages and the wisdom of elders. Some people feel both invisible, and that they are forced to disengage and retreat when they age – as society expects them to. However, this attitude is changing with the Baby Boomer generation. The Bible makes it clear that we should respect age and the wisdom of experience of the old (see, for example, Lev. 19:32).
- Health and wellbeing are influenced by the degree to which we are engaged and involved in the environment around us, social contact and an active interest in what is going on, and our relationships, as believers, vertically towards God and horizontally towards each other.[2]

DEMENTIA IS ...

Dementia is an irreversible and progressive intellectual disability affecting key functions of daily life and caused by a group of disease processes. The symptoms that all people with dementia share are the true attributes of the disease, but what they don't share can rarely be attributed to dementia. Dementia is an umbrella term which describes a serious deterioration in mental functions, such as memory, language orientation and judgment. There are many types; Alzheimer's disease accounts for two-thirds of cases, and is the best known.

Early symptoms of dementia may include loss of memory – for example, forgetting the way home from the shops, or being unable to remember names and places, or what happened earlier the same day; and mood changes – particularly as parts of the brain that control emotion are affected. People with dementia may also feel sad, frightened or angry about what is happening to them. Communication problems – a decline in the ability to talk, read and write may also be an early symptom in some forms of dementia.

Dementia is progressive, which means the symptoms will gradually get worse. How fast dementia progresses will depend on the individual, their environment and the underlying pathology. Each person is unique and will experience dementia in their own way.

WHO GETS DEMENTIA?

There are about 825,000 people in the UK with dementia; the condition is expected to double in the next forty years. Dementia mainly affects older people. However, it can affect younger people: there are approximately 15,000 in the UK under the age of sixty-five who have dementia, requiring specialist services. It can affect both men and women.[3]

Scientists are investigating the genetic background. It does appear that in a few rare cases, the diseases that cause dementia can be inherited. So, some people with a particular genetic make-up have a higher risk than others of developing the disease. But generally, there is no single factor – probably a combination; some can develop their symptoms silently, or something can trigger it.

TYPES OF DEMENTIA
ALZHEIMER'S DISEASE

Senile dementia of the Alzheimer's type is a progressive global impairment of intellectual then daily living skills, slowly eroding abilities over a period of years, arising from changes in the brain (plaques of protein in brain tissue and tangles of abnormal nerve fibres in cells). This is the most common type of dementia. It is named after the German scientist Alois Alzheimer, who identified the condition over a century ago. He studied a woman in an asylum in 1901 until her death in 1906 and found she had short-term memory loss and disorientation. After her death, he studied her brain and discovered she had protein deposits and amyloidal plaques and tangles, which characterise dementia.

Alzheimer's affects one in twenty over the age of sixty-five and one in five over the age of eighty. Risk factors include genetic inheritance (in early types particularly), also smoking, severe whiplash, head injury, high blood pressure and high cholesterol. Alzheimer's is diagnosed when other causes such as infections, vitamin insufficiency, thyroid deficiency, tumours or depression are excluded. Some drugs may be offered in the earlier stages to stabilise symptoms for a limited period.

VASCULAR DEMENTIA

Vascular dementia is the second most common type of dementia caused by problems of the blood supply to the brain. The conditions that cause or increase damage to the vascular system include high blood pressure, heart problems, high cholesterol and diabetes. It is therefore important to have these conditions treated as early as possible. There are many types of vascular dementia but the most common is caused by a single stroke or a series of small strokes, sometimes referred to as multi-infarct dementia (affecting about 20 per cent of all dementias). This type is often accompanied by slurred speech or weakness down one side of the body. The other main type is small vessel disease. It is also possible to have a combination of both types.

People with this type of dementia will experience problems with concentration, communicating, depression and memory, and they sometimes have periods of acute confusion. The stepped progression means that symptoms can remain at a constant level and then suddenly deteriorate. People with vascular dementia can also experience hallucinations, delusions, wandering and getting lost, restlessness and incontinence.

Risk factors include a history of stroke or hypertension, high cholesterol, poor physical activity, high intake of alcohol, smoking, and eating a fatty diet.[4]

LEWY BODY DISEASE

This has recently come to light and is named after the person who discovered small protein-like bodies distributed in specific parts of the brain resulting in memory loss, language and reasoning difficulties, hallucinations, delusions, fluctuation, and muscular rigidity similar to Parkinsonism, balance, tremor and slowness of movement. This can sometimes be misinterpreted as laziness. It represents 10–15 per cent of dementias.

CREUTZFELDT JAKOB DISEASE

This is a transmissible disease due to a slow 'virus' which can lie dormant for a number of years. This is caused by abnormally formed clusters of protein (prion) in the central nervous system, resulting in sponge-like holes in the brain matter. People with CJD normally die within six months; it is a very rare condition that starts with memory loss and mood changes, quickly progressing to complete loss of function and dependency requiring full nursing care.

FRONTAL LOBE DEMENTIA
(INCLUDING PICK'S DISEASE)

This is characterised by personality change such as lack of insight and empathy, inappropriate behaviour, loss of inhibitions; the sufferer becomes easily distracted and develops compulsive tendencies. In fronto-temporal dementia, damage is usually focused on the front part of the brain. At first, personality and behaviour are more affected than memory.

OTHER TYPES OF DEMENTIA

There are a number of other illnesses and chronic conditions that can also include dementia-like symptoms, often in the later stages of the illness. These include:

- late onset Parkinson's disease
- Huntington's disease
- multiple sclerosis
- thyroid deficiency
- dementia caused by head injury
- HIV-related dementia.

Dementia can also occur in those who have a history of alcohol abuse (Korsakoff's syndrome). These people find it difficult to learn new skills, lack insight into their condition, and invent stories to fill the gaps in memory (confabulation). Some recover if they stop drinking and adopt healthy living and a diet with adequate vitamins and nutrition. If they persist in drinking, they are likely to need long-term care. For example, Lucy's story:

> Last Christmas Dad's neighbour rang me, concerned she had not seen his lights on for a few days. When I turned up, I found he had collapsed on the kitchen floor with hypothermia. He had been lying there for possibly three days. After four months in hospital, we were told he had alcohol related dementia and was sectioned by the Mental Health Act before his move to a suitable residential home. It was a shock, as the signs of dementia were not at all on our radar. Dad does not know where he lives and makes up stories, as he cannot separate fact from fiction. We struggled to get information; we did not know what questions to ask or what was expected of us. But we now all have a better relationship with him than we have had for years.

Dementias present with difficulties of judgment, articulation, understanding and insight. However, other conditions can present as dementia with impairment of memory, disorientation, poor concentration, delusions and hallucinations.

COMMON MISUNDERSTANDINGS WITH DEMENTIA

The chart on the following pages shows some common misunderstandings of behaviour in daily life situations.[5]

Behaviour	Frequent explanations	Possible causes due to changes in the brain
Getting into the wrong bed/sitting in someone else's room	Lonely, disorientated or over-sexed; needing companionship	Cannot recognise the environment
Dropping things	Clumsy	Movement disorder due to changes in the brain or stroke
Not always recognising sounds or speech	Poor hearing; being difficult	Inability to recognise and interpret sounds or language
Unable to converse but able to sing without any problem, eg hymns, songs	Attention-seeking or uncooperative	Language problem due to brain damage, but the areas in the brain responsible for melody and rhythm not damaged (they are located in another part of the brain)
Unable to get dressed	'Senile', lazy, attention-seeking	Dressing apraxia, a condition of the brain which leaves a person not knowing how to perform particular actions previously learnt in daily living skills, or movement disorder

Behaviour	Frequent explanations	Possible causes due to changes in the brain
Repeating the same words over and over again	'Senile'	Damage to the front part, or the language part, of the brain
Bumping into things	Blind; forgetful	Unable to recognise objects, or to see the whole of the visual field in front due to changes in the brain affecting the way the environment is interpreted
Accusing people of assault	Troublemaker	Inability to recognise difference between themselves or others
Does not recognise faces	Rude; apathetic; blind	Inability to recognise faces due to brain damage

IS THERE A CURE?

Most forms of dementia cannot be cured, although research is continuing into developing drugs, vaccines and treatments. Drugs have been developed that can temporarily alleviate some of the symptoms of some types of dementia, particularly for moderate stages. These drugs are known as acetylcholinesterase inhibitors; people with vascular dementia are not normally given these drugs.

The National Institute for Health and Clinical Excellence (NICE) revised guidance on acetylcholinesterase inhibitors to treat some types of dementia (issued in 2006) recommends that people in the moderate stages of dementia should be given treatment with one of those drugs (see www.alzheimers.org.uk).

DEPRESSION AND DEMENTIA

Depression is a common side-effect of the disease. However, depression can sometimes be mistaken for dementia, as in an older person depression can cause impairment of cognitive (thinking) function and mimic dementia, and it is difficult to distinguish between them. But there are some important distinctions as the following table shows.[6]

Pseudodementia	Dementia
Onset can be dated with precision	Onset can be dated only within broad limits
Rapid progression of symptoms after onset	Slow progression
History of previous psychiatric condition	Slow progression of symptoms
Person complains of much cognitive loss	Person complains little of cognitive loss
Person emphasises disability	Person conceals disability
Little effort to perform tasks	Considerable effort to perform tasks
Strong sense of distress	Often apparent unconcern
'Don't know' answers typical	Near miss answers frequent
Attention and concentration often well preserved	Attention and concentration usually impaired

Pseudodementia	Dementia
Memory loss for recent and remote events usually equally severe	Memory loss for recent events usually more severe than for remote events

CAN DEMENTIA BE PREVENTED?

It is likely that lifestyle affects the probability of dementia; especially, as we have seen above, in vascular dementia. Other preventative factors suggest a link with:

- Good education and social class;
- The size of the hippocampus (part of the brain responsible for memory), important for retention;
- Staying mentally active: mental exercises can also help to prevent deterioration, audio visual games, reading, board games (use it or lose it);
- Staying socially connected.

Other helpful preventative measures include:

- Regular sleep;
- Avoiding chronic stress;
- Avoiding obesity;
- Meditation, prayer and reflection to nurture inner peace;
- Keeping blood pressure and cholesterol low;
- Physical activity such as dancing: 'think movement', exercising for thirty minutes five times a week, building strength, co-ordination and flexibility. Increasing the oxygen levels to the brain increases brain activity and helps alertness.[7]

OPTIMISING MEMORY

The best conditions for a good memory prevailing into later life are good general health, a relatively relaxed and stress-free environment and an active, stimulating daily life.

CONCLUSION

It's easy for older people to feel invisible, even more so when their identity is challenged by a series of losses, or relentless caring roles, lack of support or by being generally unappreciated by society. Stereotyping and ageism can lead people into nihilistic responses such as 'What do you expect at my/his/her age?' This disabling attitude can severely limit the quality of life.

However, when older people feel they are valuable, worthwhile members of society, they are more likely to have good mental and physical health.

ACTIVITY

Imagine you are aware that your mental powers are changing. You cannot seem to recognise people who say they know you; you get tongue-tied when you try to find words to express yourself. You think the place you are living in is not your home, and you don't know how you came to be there. Then a stranger comes to the door and tells you it's time for a bath. How do you think you might feel? Write down some of the emotions you could experience.

REFLECTION

Consider your own attitude to ageing. Do you think that being older can make us not only more invisible but also out of touch and irrelevant to today's society? That an older person's moral values and beliefs have no relevance in today's world? Do you believe that 'when you get old, you get forgetful' and that older people become easily confused? How would you feel if you were viewed in this way?

PRAYER

Thank You, Father God, for Your love and care for all who trust in You. Thank You that You promise: 'Even to your old age and grey hairs I am he, I am he who will sustain you. I have made you and I will carry you; I will sustain you and I will rescue you' (Isa. 46:4). Help us to be compassionate and respectful towards those who are older than us, whether they are ill, or whether they are well. Thank You, Jesus. Amen.

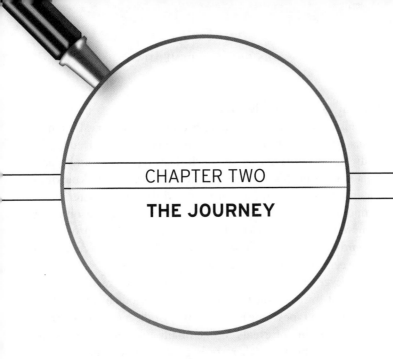

CHAPTER TWO

THE JOURNEY

'Never will I leave you; never will I forsake you.'
(Hebrews 13:5)

INTRODUCTION

It's helpful to remember that there are stereotyped beliefs, fears and ageist attitudes within our wider society, and that these will influence to a great extent how we react to issues of dementia.

It's not uncommon for people to be concerned they have dementia, particularly if they notice deterioration in their memory. However, becoming forgetful can be due to other things, such as normal ageing, stress, depression and occasionally vitamin deficiency or a tumour. So, before we look into the journey with dementia, let us think about what memory is, and how it works.

MEMORY AND HOW IT WORKS

There is more unknown than known when it comes to memory.

It's an extraordinarily complex mechanism of interacting systems which can only be described in a limited way. In simple terms, the information from the environment is received by the body through the senses of touch, hearing, vision and smell. This is then processed through the short-term (also known as the primary or working) memory which holds material for temporary or immediate use only, as in learning, reasoning or comprehension. One part of the system deals with the processing of words, letters and numbers; another, visual images controlled by the central memory store (memory executive).

However, our long-term memory comprises recording and storage of information for much longer periods of time. There are two main types. One is known as *episodic* memory, referring to the recording of events in one's daily life; the second is the *semantic* memory, which records general knowledge – factual information about the world around us.

Memory time frames are divided into:

1. Immediate working memory: where information is stored for a few seconds, such as a phone number from a directory.
2. Short-term/recent memory: this relates to information of events lasting over a few days or weeks.
3. Delayed memory: events happening in the recent few minutes are retrieved for a short while later.
4. Prospective memory: when you remind yourself of things you have to do in the future, such as turning off the cooker.
5. Long-term memory: a separate system that stores information until it is needed again.

Different aspects of memory will include facts such as specific knowledge, personal experiences and a skill, process or routine; for example, how to swim or use the computer.

The main types of memory can be categorised into visual (patterns, faces and maps) and verbal (spoken instruction).

A functioning memory requires *input* of information, *categorising* of this information, and then *storage* followed by *retrieval* when needed.

In simple terms, this is like a building, which becomes a library once the books are in it (input). These books must be ordered on every subject you can imagine. Crate-loads of these books arrive but need to be categorised by the librarian (encoding). In order to do this, the books are sorted into piles according to their topic and sub-topics and then laid out in an accessible fashion (storage). Now they are ready for the shelves which are labelled for easy access, so the public are guided to the relevant place to find what they are looking for (retrieval).[1]

MEMORY IN NORMAL AGEING

Normal ageing slows down the efficiency of the memory, and affects the ability to find words, inspect mental images, recall and, to some extent, it affects recognition, the ability to remember something that needs to be done in the future (prospective memory), and concentration, due to less efficient processes of recall of detail. Once this happens, to a varied extent in each individual, most people will start to use compensatory knowledge and strategies to help them, such as diaries, lists or other reminders. Both physical and cognitive function change as we get older. Fluid intelligence and the capacity to respond rapidly and flexibly gradually diminish, while crystallised intelligence, the residue of previous learning, can continue to increase. Semantic memory continues to grow but it is less easy to access.

The likelihood of dementia increases with age, but as a condition it eventually devastates the memory inexorably, in particular categorising (encoding). Information can be stored relatively well once the information has been encoded. Recall is severely affected but can be helped by the use of various types of cues (visual, auditory and other forms of sensory 'triggers').

MEMORY AND DEMENTIA

People with dementia retain their long-term store of memory the longest, and lose short-term; other cognitive aspects are affected, such as verbal fluency and language, orientation in time and place, control of movement and action, attention, visual perception (such as depth), problem-solving and social functioning. This broadly results in social withdrawal and dependency on others.

Dementia is sometimes diagnosed in memory clinics. Alzheimer's disease is not easy to diagnose other than at a post-mortem, in which a patient is found to have the characteristic plaques and neurofibrillary tangles. Diagnosis requires behavioural and psychological examination and the discounting of other possible causes. A diagnosis is usually given when a person performs lower than the bottom 5 per cent of the population in two of the above cognitive areas of function.

Memory clinics offer formal systematic monitoring of mental state at intervals and can be used to test drugs, assess cognitive and daily living function and any behaviour changes, with a view to early diagnosis and support; this can be in the form of counselling and support for carers.

HOW DO YOU KNOW IF YOU HAVE DEMENTIA?

GPs are receiving new guidance for early diagnosis so it is worth discussing any anxieties with them. Getting a proper diagnosis is important and will help prescribe the right treatment and prepare for the long term. The GP might make a referral to a geriatrician, neurologist or psychiatrist who will carry out a number of tests, testing memory and the ability to carry out normal daily tasks.

TYPICAL SYMPTOMS OF DEMENTIA

- In Alzheimer's disease and some other types of dementia memory loss predominates: especially for recent events; person can misplace objects or forget what they were about to do.
- Getting lost or disorientated, especially in new environments.
- Difficulty finding the right words.
- Poor concentration.
- Difficulties taking on board new ideas or learning a new skill.
- Poor judgment and thinking abilities such as sequencing, eg laying a table.
- Psychological mood changes; irritation, saying inappropriate things, becoming suspicious or aggressive.
- Personality changes.
- Misinterpretation of events.

Later on, as the disease progresses, further intellectual, behavioural and physical problems are experienced, affecting speech, language, mobility, continence, frailty and general daily living skills. Walking or wandering (a determination to keep on the move in a dogged fashion or apparently aimlessly) can be due to several things: an unfamiliar place, feeling restricted, medication use, negative carer attitude leading to anxiety, searching for something. It could also be alleviating emotional stress, or communicating a need such as lack of exercise or attention, discomfort, lack of stimulation in the environment or body clock changes – or a combination.[2]

COMMUNICATION DIFFICULTIES[3]

Those with dementia will experience increasing problems understanding what is being said to them and what is going on around them. They are likely to find it difficult to communicate with other people. They may gradually lose their speech, or they may repeat a few words, or even cry out from time to time. However, verbal language is only one way of communicating. Their expression and body language may give clues about how they are feeling.

Some of the specific difficulties in communication include:

- Confusing the past reality with present reality.
- Problems remembering normal routines, appointments and services used.
- Communicating thoughts and feelings.
- Varying awareness levels.
- Physical and social environment disorientation.

It is also true to say that people with dementia can be undermined by the behaviour and negative attitudes of others towards them; for example, withholding affection; banishing them from social situations; talking about them in front of them as if they were not there; treating them as an object. These behaviours are linked to our values about the intrinsic worth of a person – valuing them as God values them; what they are challenging in us about compassion and humility.[4]

The person with dementia may have problems with ideas, words, speech and possibly hearing, so carers can find themselves dealing with issues such as repetition, confusion (person, time or place), instigating and continuing a conversation, making decisions, dwelling on the past, forgetting mid-flow what is being spoken about, overreaction, difficulties in finding words.[5]

INFLUENCING FACTORS IN COMMUNICATION

People with dementia experience mood swings, so those who care for them need to be aware of nuances of behaviour; they are influenced by physical (pain, discomfort etc), social/emotional (quality of relationship, presence of others, spiritual needs) and temporal factors (pacing, timing, concentration etc). Other difficulties they might experience could be:

- Reduced insight and awareness of problems.
- Memory recall/retrieval.
- Slowing down of conversations.
- Repetition.
- Saying things that are not based on the reality of the listener.
- Inability to convey much information.
- Possible difficulties with reading or writing.
- Poor eye contact.

If the person with dementia has a visual or hearing impairment, they might experience further additional barriers. The isolation might include lack of awareness of the environment, leading to a fear of falling and accidents, anxiety and withdrawal, less opportunity for participation, reduced involvement in activities, and unco-operative behaviour.

UNDERSTANDING THE EXPERIENCE

On the *Daily Mail* website (11 December 2009), an article written by author Terry Pratchett, who has a type of early onset Alzheimer's, was headed 'I'm slipping away a bit at a time and all I can do is watch it happen' – an apt description of dementia. One could also say it is like taking a disturbing journey.

Imagine you leave home to walk to the shops. The street, the houses and gardens are familiar, and you feel relaxed. You meet with neighbours along the way, and pass the time of day. But as you walk on, something changes. You notice the houses and the gardens don't look quite as you remember them. You stop a neighbour and ask if everything is all right; they haven't noticed anything strange, and say so. As you walk along further, you begin to realise that everything seems unfamiliar. You speak to a woman in her garden; she frowns, and when she replies, she doesn't speak English. As you struggle to understand, she looks at you with pity. You don't know what to make of this, so ask her to tell you exactly where you are. But this time, your own words don't seem to make sense …

SELF-ESTEEM

Once a diagnosis has been given, people are likely to experience a serious sense of loss.[6]

- *Loss of intellectual ability*: short-term memory, making logical connections.
- *Reduced communication ability*: due to poor concentration and language difficulties.
- *Reduced independence*: requiring supervision in activities and problems of getting lost.

These combine to create the conditions for depression, frustration, poor self-esteem and anxiety about what the future might hold, or a sense of failure and discouragement. This is particularly the case for those who are given an early diagnosis. Self-esteem is important to maintain relationships, and prevent social withdrawal and loss of confidence, staying connected with familiar activities that help to create a sense of identity, belonging and connection. Receiving reassurance and feeling valued and that their life matters is important to the person with dementia, helping them to feel they can still contribute, and are not alone.

STIGMA

And of course, there is the stigma of dementia to deal with – how people react to the diagnosis. This is Michaela's experience:

> When my mother was diagnosed with vascular dementia, people suddenly didn't seem to know how to relate to her – or even how to speak to me about her. When I was shopping in the town where she'd lived for nearly thirty years, people who had known her would ask about her, but when I suggested they visit, they were clearly uncomfortable with the idea and most of them shied away. I found this very frustrating. I wanted to shout, 'She's still the same person, you know – and she'd enjoy some company. OK, there are things she can't do any more. But she still loves a joke, a cup of tea and a chat. Please don't shut her out. Please don't stop being her friend.'

EFFECTS OF DEMENTIA ON FAMILIES

The diagnosis can be devastating for the family of the person who has dementia, and the effects can be cataclysmic, involving anxiety, anger, frustration, loneliness, tiredness, guilt and grief. In these times, our faith becomes very important, for God can draw very near, and we need to learn to lean hard on Him daily: 'Give us each day our daily bread' (Luke 11:3). See Appendix 1.

- **Anxiety**: Being a carer for a person with dementia might mean the person becoming more dependent or challenging in their needs, and along with a lack of information or support this can cause anxiety.
- **Anger**: Unrealistic demands or expectations from the person or the wider family, overwork, lack of emotional support,

lack of professional help when it's needed ... can all cause anger which may be expressed in different forms, both subtle and overt aggression. (Professional help and intervention is needed where there is a risk or history of violence or aggressive relationships.)

- **Loneliness/aloneness**: Isolation and lack of time, energy or opportunity for other meaningful relationships to continue.
- **Frustration**: Unfulfilled hopes, lack of responsive information or care, long waits for support, lack of support from other family members. This can develop into anger or depression in troubled times.
- **Tiredness**: Fatigue looking after a dependent person, lack of energy to carry out the level of care or nursing required without sufficient breaks or practical help (equipment or people). Prolonged tiredness can lead to illness and a subsequent breakdown of care.
- **Guilt**: Guilt and lack of motivation are often associated with an experience of powerlessness, a sense of hopelessness, lack of daily structure and roles, limited social opportunities, low self-esteem or lack of confidence, unchallenging and limited opportunity. Although a carer may not be responsible for the deterioration in health of their loved one, it is not uncommon for them to feel guilt as a sense of failure, regret: 'If only I had done x or y ...' or guilt in simply continuing to enjoy something that their relative cannot do any more, or when they 'give in' to respite care, thinking they are 'putting their relative away'. Here it is good to talk to other care-givers/relatives in the same situation. The Relatives and Residents Association has some useful leaflets and an advice line, as have other charities such as Carers UK or Counsel and Care, the Alzheimer's Society locally. (See Contacts on pp.109ff.)

- **Loss/Grief**: This is often experienced where a carer feels they have lost a friend or equal partner in a relationship, especially if they are not recognised by the loved one any more. The support of an Alzheimer's group locally provides help and an opportunity to share feelings in a trusted environment.[7]

WHO CARES FOR THE CARER?

Jean's husband is in the mid stages of Alzheimer's disease. They are both in their early seventies and have the support of Bob's widowed sister who lives with them. Their children are grown up and live nearby. Jean can leave her husband with the support of her sister-in-law and a visit from the local 'Crossroads'[8] visiting scheme. But Jean is finding every day a struggle; she lacks pleasure in life, which has become a set of chores, with the additional disappointment from the lack of fulfilled retirement plans. She is finding herself acting less as a wife and more as a mother to a man whose skills and memory are disappearing with each passing month.

Preserving relationships is important in caring situations. There are complex issues which will be unique to every situation, and may include:

- Loss of a companionship and former relationship and the accompanying grief; role changes.
- Loss of a future planned together.
- Loss of a lifestyle once taken for granted.
- Challenges posed by a new role in an unfamiliar area.
- Having control over another person's life.
- Dealing with manipulation and emotional blackmail.
- Dealing with accusations from a loved one who is likely

to feel insecure or fearful of the unknown, or being separated from their family and familiar home surroundings if a care home is involved.
- Feeling inadequate or trapped.[9]

The effects of dependency on the carer as the condition progresses may include some of the following experiences:

- The carer's physical health suffering.
- There could be a health risk, whereby the person needing help refuses to eat, or take medication, or refuses physical care, which results in a deteriorating condition.
- The person with dementia might open doors to strangers; wander, get lost, leave the gas on or smoke in the bedroom.
- Physical deterioration – the carer may not be able to continue to manage either the extent of emotional or physical care required. (There might also be a lack of adequate community care available to meet needs required to enable the carer to continue caring.)
- Emotional equilibrium – any aspect of change can affect sleep, eating, energy levels, normal healthy activity, or can lead to depression.
- Feeling resentful, angry, short-tempered after a difficult period on inadequate support; if these feelings become noticeable and sustained, the person with dementia could be at risk of abuse due to the overwhelming stress.
- Lack of insight into a condition or coping with someone who is unrealistic about their capabilities can result in others being at risk.

GPs and social workers may notice changes in the one with dementia and the carer, and seeing things more objectively, may suggest that this is the time to consider other options, such as long-term care. It is important to remember that being a martyr, refusing help or not dealing with feelings of guilt can result in stress which can affect both physical and mental health, and might lead on to other health issues such as blood pressure or cardiac problems.[10]

CONCLUSION

The dementia journey is long and hard for the individual and carer alike. The challenge for those with dementia, and their carers, is how to preserve their sense of who they are (identity), maintain connection in relationship with others within the poetry and tragedy of dementia, give hope, and maintain 'personhood' and a real experience of unconditional love. Also, how to help preserve their intrinsic God-given human worth in the face of such a destructive condition so that we can help the person with dementia to wear their age as a crown and not as a burden.

ACTIVITY

Consider the following poem about the experience of dementia. What are the key messages the poet is trying to communicate about their world and what is important to them? Think about how we can reach a person from their world rather than ours. What could we do to relieve their pain and anxiety?

It comes again relentlessly
The shredding of my thoughts
This disappearing sense of me
And who I am or was

The window opens inches wide
Behind the blanks of dark
I fear the breaking cordless sash
That shuts me out at once

My anxious capsule gripping tight
So seldom yields away
My lucid moments filled with fear
A constant crippling pain

The gentle aura of your touch
The respite of your hands
My present moments feel the calm
And I know who I am

Patricia Duncan Duff, January 2008

Write your own poem or some prose about your own experiences of dementia.

REFLECTION

Think about the experience of Michaela, under 'Stigma' (p.35). Why do you think people behave like this regarding people with dementia? Reflect on the fact that God knows and accepts us just as we are. If it helps, read Psalm 139, meditating on verses 1–4,7,11–14 (see also Appendix 1).

PRAYER

O God, my God, I praise You that You understand that which I do not. Thank You that You promise never to leave me or to forsake me; that You say You will be with me always. Thank You, Lord.

CHAPTER THREE

DEMENTIA CARE 1: TREATMENT

'Trust in the LORD with all your heart and lean not
on your own understanding; in all your ways acknowledge him,
and he will make your paths straight.'
(Proverbs 3:5–6)

INTRODUCTION

People with dementia have a disability. However, their personal identity can be maintained through meaningful engagement with others, and activities, and we should remember that as well as physical needs, their psychological and emotional needs are just as vital. Once there has been a diagnosis, the issue of preserving identity, developing relationships and using retained abilities can help people to form a real sense of 'who they are'.

In good dementia care, the focus should be on enhancing wellbeing and reducing ill-being. (We will look at issues of wellbeing and ill-being further in Chapter Four.)

CHANGING ATTITUDES TOWARD DEMENTIA CARE[1]

Old culture of Dementia Care	New culture of Dementia Care
• Dementia is an undemanding field to work in, few skills are needed	• An exciting area of practice requiring high skill levels
• It is a progressive, degenerative disease and no action can be taken to make a difference	• Dementia is a disability and wellbeing depends on the quality of care provided
• The expertise lies only with doctors and scientists	• Care-givers are experts
• Research is based on cures and treatments	• Research should aim to develop quality care
• Care culture of 'them and us'	• Staff seen as equals replaces the 'them and us' culture
• Care is limited to meeting physical needs and emphasising what a person could not do/ decline	• Care priority to enhance personhood and address both emotional and physical needs Intervention is based on what a person *can* do, considering beliefs, values and interests
• Problem behaviour needs to be 'managed'/controlled	• All behaviour has meaning which needs to be understood by responding to the underlying needs and feelings being communicated
• Carers put aside personal feelings and concentrate on the job in hand	• Care-givers need to be in touch with their feelings • Management needs to enable development

The old medical model has been significantly criticised as it is more concerned about the person with *dementia* than the *person* with dementia. It also limits the wider appreciation of the importance of the social environment, the relevance of individual past history and future circumstances, or the subjective experience for the person, as well as the connection between intellectual behavioural change and neurology. The new culture sees the condition as complex and takes into account home, family and wider relationships, the influence of beliefs and life experience, and emotional responses. Significantly, it recognises the importance of people continuing to be helped to communicate their needs, and how legitimate attempts to do this in the face of cognitive decline must be better understood and supported. Given the right conditions, there can be a delay in the rate of decline, and an improvement in function and wellbeing.

The 'Biomedical' approach has now shifted to the person-centred care promoted by the late Tom Kitwood (he was Professor of Psychogerontology at Bradford University, a practising psychotherapist and founder of the Bradford Dementia Group), and emphasises the experience of the individual *person* behind the illness. It is shaped by a number of unique individual factors such as a person's past life history, their personality, general health, specific neurological damage and the effects of the surrounding social environment, and significantly, the importance of unconditional love (how a person relates, communicates, compensates, makes sense and responds to change). There are positive ways in which the experience of the person can change and move from a state of ill-being to wellbeing. We will look more into this in the next chapter.

TREATMENT AND SUPPORT

1. MEDICATION

In the early stages, there are some drugs available to halt progression of some forms of the disease. In the later stages, often once people are in continuing care settings, medication may be given for behaviour which is challenging to others, such as agitation, aggression, shouting, delusions and psychotic symptoms, which 90 per cent of those with dementia will have. The use of antipsychotics in dementia is under review. Sometimes this behaviour can be due to communication difficulties and a misinterpretation of needs. All these symptoms can fluctuate and eventually burn out; that is, they are not ongoing or persistent. Latest evidence suggests powerful sedative drugs are given too early for people in care homes, without first trying other approaches: research shows that two-thirds of people are not distressed by psychotic symptoms, and many behaviours are situation-specific. Of those in care homes 40 per cent are prescribed tranquilising drugs such as Risperidone. These drugs are used widely to treat symptoms but have powerful negative side-effects such as reducing mobility, doubling cognitive decline, increasing the likelihood of a stroke; they are considered as not acceptable therapies and should only be used in severe cases as a last resort.

2. COUNSELLING IN THE EARLY STAGES

Counselling helps people to understand what's happening to them, what to expect, and what this will mean for the individual and their family; options for the future should be discussed at this stage. Often people feel guilty that they cannot remember things. Creating a life history can help retain the individual's personhood, reminds them of achievements and significant life events, and gives a sense of connection to family and significant others. As a tool, it can provide an opportunity to express feelings and reminisce.

Counselling can also help people in the early stages with maintaining social contacts, by working with others with dementia who can discuss the embarrassment of forgetting names, maintaining conversation, feeling a burden, forgetting what to do in familiar situations, and so on. Specialist counselling can help to give practical advice, such as understanding powers of attorney, benefits, advocacy, or helping plan the future. It is important for the counsellor to work with family carers so they can understand the precise difficulties experienced.

Deeper forms of psychotherapeutic counselling can address loss, bereavement and traumatic life events that can easily rise, out of context, to the surface, as a person moves between different worlds and time frames of their reality.

3. A POSITIVE OCCUPATIONAL AND SOCIAL ENVIRONMENT

This means having emotional and practical support in the provision of activities to retain interests within capabilities; having meaningful roles, sufficient stimulation and activity choices; being included in social situations, addressing 'neutral' daily experiences and turning them into 'positive social encounters'; the prevention of loneliness, helplessness and boredom. All of this provides care in the new culture. This is particularly important for people in care homes.

Other approaches that address quality social interaction, communication and positive engagement with people include meaningful activities such as music and stimulating conversation. This can improve behaviour and enrich quality of life, if applied in a systematic way. This is a challenge in some care homes where the staffing levels and training are minimal. This is why quality of life in care homes is a major strand of the new dementia strategy. The turnover rate of staff working with dementia is often high, affecting continuity – particularly important for people with dementia.

4. POSITIVE COMMUNICATION

This is at the heart of care-giving (taking into consideration additional acquired hearing difficulties associated with age, such as loss of high frequency sounds which can reduce the ability to understand words). A person with dementia requires relationships and people who meet them in their present along the spectrum of 'time travel'. Using a running commentary of what is about to happen, what is happening now, and reminding a person what has just happened, can help to navigate and orientate. This provides a sense of security, involvement and continuity. Good practice in dementia care promotes:

- Person-centred and relationship-centred approaches;
- Commitment to 24-hour engagement;
- Four-point assessment – personality, health, biography, cognitive capacity;
- Four levels of engagement (four cognitive levels, the Pool Activity Levels (PAL). See Appendix 4.);
- The therapeutic use of self.

5. PROMOTING HEALTH FOR PEOPLE WITH DEMENTIA

a) Maintaining physical activity

- improves mental health (confidence, self-esteem, socialisation and motivation)
- increases physical function – fitness, stamina, flexibility, balance and co-ordination
- reduces hidden pain and discomfort

- reduces social isolation (if a group activity)
- reduces falls risk
- reduces health inequalities, providing more opportunities
- increases efficient respiration
- improves wellbeing and mood
- improves circulation
- improves neuro-muscular efficiency and co-ordination
- stimulates cortex of the brain
- stimulates the immune system
- develops positive self-image and confidence.

One of the great ways of promoting health is a walking group. This can end, in the early stages, with a social drink and chat. As the condition progresses, there are creative ways to encourage movement using music and colourful apparatus, eg balls, scarves and batons, or physical games, individually or in small groups. In later stages, providing quality time, ensuring people are moved regularly, offering hand massage and sensory stimulation can also be helpful. People with dementia are 40 to 60 per cent more likely to fall due to additional neurological changes affecting balance and how they interpret their environment differently, and walk in a less regulated way. Increased risk needs to be assessed individually.

Physical activity may include actions that are a part of daily living, such as cooking, cleaning, walking to the shops or climbing the stairs. As people get older they tend to decrease the amount of habitual physical activity they do. Therefore, if older people are to achieve the recommended levels, there is a need to increase the amount of both their intentional and habitual physical activity. With so many labour-saving devices and well-intentioned help in daily living tasks, there's a danger that frail older people will perform minimal physical activity; they need support and encouragement to help them remain functioning independently. But how much physical activity is enough?

There are no national guidelines in the UK for physical activity specific to older people yet, but in 2004, the Department of Health recommended the adult population to take part in: '30 minutes of moderate physical activity on at least five occasions a week – for example brisk walking'.[2] To benefit health, physical activity should be at an intensity that raises the heart rate sufficiently to leave the individual breathing more heavily than normal, and feeling warmer. While the recommendation is moderate activity for half an hour on five days of the week, it should be acknowledged that any activity is better than none and the greatest gains are achieved when a sedentary person is encouraged to become a little more active more often. For many, thirty minutes of activity will always be impossible; however, a 'bit at a time' approach where minutes of activity are accumulated throughout the day rather than in a single bout will also contribute to the daily amount of activity needed.

b) Nutrition
It is very important to maintain balanced nutritional intake. Personal likes and dislikes should be known and accomodated, especially in care homes.

c) Cognitive stimulation and rehabilitation
There are a variety of exercises to stimulate the brain, such as revisiting memories, particularly as the senses are stimulated and new memories are triggered. Various techniques can be used to assist memory training, such as using visual cues.

d) Early detection of pain
As 50 per cent of people over sixty-five may experience a pain-

causing condition, it is important to consider the presence of pain which can be difficult to express. Older people have the additional barriers of ageism, leading to dismissive attitudes, stoicism, and a negative culture of care.

e) Environment enrichment
Providing a socially enriched environment can minimise aggression and improve opportunities for continued social involvement. It is critical in maintaining communication, and includes having opportunities to engage with people, things of interest to see, do and touch, encouragement to maintain abilities in daily living skills, make choices, and have information broken down in ways that are easy to understand. Attention to hearing, eyesight and dentures is also important.

Meal times provide opportunities to be imaginative – smelling food, laying the table with attention to details, maximising the rituals around a meal. This is particularly important for people living in long-term care settings. Here are some guidelines for carers:

- Use a positive and gentle approach.
- Introduce different sensations slowly, to prevent overwhelming with stimuli.
- Consider individual needs.
- Explore different combinations to encourage stimulation and imagination where appropriate.
- Encourage a sense of adventure and delight.

f) Empathy techniques
Validation has replaced Reality Orientation, an approach where people were constantly reminded and corrected regarding information about the day, date, time, place and matters of

current interest. Correcting people led to confronting them with painful truths and reliving loss which precipitated high levels of grief and anxiety. Naomi Feil[3] devised a combined verbal and non-verbal approach for carers to help the person with dementia by understanding the underlying emotional need, and responding with techniques that assist the person in expressing their emotions, according to their stage of dementia, and based on a good understanding of their life story and former life roles. We can redefine CARE this way:

- **C**ommunication that is sensitive.
- **A**bility-focused practice, with activity central to care.
- **R**estorative, relationship-focused.
- **E**nablement, empathy and engagement.

g) Person-centred care
This is a psycho-therapeutic approach supporting preserving individual identity, dignity and respect, as well as helping carers to understand people in the context of their past, their former life pattern, roles, interests and preferences, to positively maintain personhood. Person-centred theory defines dementia in the following way:

Dementia = personality, biography, health, neurological impairment, social psychology[4]

CONCLUSION
To provide best quality care we must understand that *dementia is not an unchangeable illness* where nothing can be done. It is a *disability* which is made up of a person's *unique life history, personality, general health, specific damage to a part of the brain* and the *attitudes of those caring for them.*

So, dementia is a disability, and in the treatment and support of a person with dementia, wellbeing can be improved, and personhood maintained. We need to remember that all behaviour is meaningful and needs to be understood, not just managed; emotional needs are as important as physical needs. Simply put, good care is about preserving the person behind the disability.

ACTIVITY

Life histories inform and provide clues to familiar and previously enjoyed activity, but it's also important to observe what 'sets someone alight' in the present. Think about a person you know who has dementia. What practical ideas could you employ to celebrate their lives?

- Make up a scrapbook using postcards, certificates, maps, mementoes etc.
- Keep a diary, illustrated with pictures/photographs.
- Compose a collage using objects or picture symbols representing different aspects of the person's life.
- Make a Memory Box, incorporating objects representing any aspect or interest.

REFLECTION
Loss of Self
I sit alone, your hand in mine
And strive to see your face
But spattered blocks of recall lost
Deny my anxious quest.

I must go home to where I was
Before the shutters closed,
Fragmenting thoughts with fear entwine,
As isolation grows

I'll meet my friends of yesterday
I feel their love from then,
I feel the joy of joining in
Then glimpse my world of now

Is this your hand I hold in mine?
Its warmth feels safe within,
A moment's grace from ceaseless loss
When emptiness begins.

Patricia Duncan Duff, 2007

Reflect on the words of the poem. How do you think it must feel to 'lose yourself'? Read Psalm 88, and Micah 6:8. Then spend some time in prayer, perhaps asking God to give you wisdom in how best to support the person you know who has dementia.

PRAYER

Loving heavenly Father, help us always to remember that the *person* with dementia is dearly loved and esteemed by You. Help us to know the best way to support our loved ones on this difficult journey. Thank You that each is precious to You, and honoured in Your sight (Isa. 43:4); that You know, that You care, that You created and formed us, that You have summoned us by name, and we are Yours (Isa. 43:1). Amen.

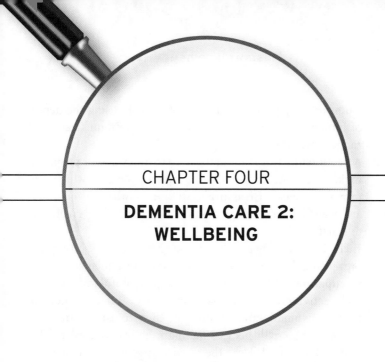

CHAPTER FOUR

DEMENTIA CARE 2: WELLBEING

'Even to your old age … I am he who will sustain you. I have made
you and I will carry you; I will sustain you and I will rescue you.'
(Isaiah 46:4)

INTRODUCTION

For the person with dementia it is important that *wellbeing* is
promoted. This can be carried out by maintaining the person's
physical and mental 'wellness', and by improving their daily
social and psychological experiences. It's important that we help
them keep their self-esteem; this can be done by the person feeling
they are part of a group, they have a role, and are recognised and
respected.

Tom Kitwood suggested principles essential to the core human
need for love[1]:

1. **Comfort** – by providing a sense of security using the depth of human closeness and warmth, often communicated in a range of ways.
2. **Attachment** – this is about the need to find ways for people to make special attachments with people and objects, which can provide a sense of reassurance. Good 'mothering' qualities are needed as psychological safety is necessary for creativity to function.
3. **Inclusion** – helping people to be involved socially with others, preventing them from withdrawing back into themselves.
4. **Occupation** – helping people to have purposeful involvement with activities, which have importance and relevance to them individually, and encouraging them to use abilities and interests. This will help to maintain ability and raise self-esteem and mood. Here the word *engagement* is important to think about. It is not just about having something to do; the quality of any creative activity is about a wholehearted absorption, being fully and wholly involved and being 'caught up in the action'.
5. **Identity** – working hard to develop relationships using communication in its fullest sense and developing meaningful roles, working with what the person is still able to do, can help them form a sense of who they are as unique individuals as a link with the past is made. For example, if they liked being helpful, we can encourage this in activities they are still able to manage. Keeping contact with others helps to maintain personhood. The focus should be on reducing ill-being and enhancing wellbeing, which can be improved in spite of cognitive difficulties. Emotional and psychological needs are as important as the physical ones; careful listening and interpreting of behaviour is significant, as all behaviour has meaning for the individual. We should try to understand

what the person is attempting to communicate rather than simply resorting to managing or controlling their behaviour.

SIGNS OF WELLBEING AND ILL-BEING

A person's wellbeing can be improved by helping them participate in an activity or by helping them to express themselves. Their level of wellbeing can be shown through outward signs; examples are listed below. The signs observed can tell us how much the person is engaging in the activity, how they are expressing themselves, and how much they are enjoying socialising. The higher the levels of these the better the wellbeing experienced by an individual. The signs of wellbeing:

- A relaxed body
- An ability to express emotions
- Sensitivity to a situation
- Helpful behaviour
- Showing humour
- Showing pleasure
- Showing affection
- Initiating social contact
- Helpfulness
- Self-respect
- Love
- Values/beliefs
- Hope
- Joy
- Creativity
- Wonder–worship
- Peace
- Positive approach to diminishment in health[2]

A person will show the following signs if they are experiencing ill-being, which can be caused by social isolation and disengagement:

- Anxiety and fear
- Boredom
- Apathy
- Physical discomfort or pain
- Withdrawal
- Despair
- Anger[3]

KEEPING SOCIALLY ENGAGED
ENJOYING ACTIVITIES

One of the keys to maintaining wellbeing is to be found in involving the person with dementia in day-to-day meaningful activities (see Chapter Five, where we will look at activities within occupational therapy). Different types of activity may vary according to the changing needs and preferences of the person, but they should encourage creativity, cultural interest, self-esteem, emotional expression and mood, intellectual/cognitive stimulation, physical activity, relaxation and recreation, sensory experience, social interaction and connection with community/family and, finally, spiritual expression. Activities can help provide a structure to the day and give a person a sense of belonging. They are a chance to reduce restlessness and agitation, and provide opportunities for both verbal and non-verbal communication. (For example, music, which can be enjoyed at a variety of levels, is essential for those lost in the maelstrom of dementia.) All activities should aim to raise wellbeing.

People with dementia function at different levels and require more emotional and sensory support as they move into a later stage of progression. We need to consider a person's interests, background and personality type; the important principle is to join people where they are in time and place, and consider the world from their perspective. Looking at them within the context of their values, beliefs, life experience, roles, personality type and preferences helps us to understand them, and provide activities that have personal meaning. There are tools that can assist in delivering activities effectively by assessing the correct level and in monitoring/evaluating activities for those caring for people with dementia. Providing activities at the right level for their stage of dementia within an environment that enables and encourages participation involves some additional knowledge in proven approaches. These can be incorporated into everyday activities such as reminiscence, stimulating the mind and senses, and validation (empathy). Encouraging brief and familiar enjoyable and individually relevant experiences requires carers to have an *animated, joyous* disposition, particularly as the disability increases; this requires empathy, non-verbal communication and the use of all the sensory modalities. Enjoyable activities require the utilisation of all channels of communication as an art form which takes time to develop, both verbally and non-verbally, engaging the preferred senses as a deeper understanding of the individual grows.

Activities are like ecosystems, and should reflect the natural rhythms of life, providing opportunities for companionship and reciprocal relationships; this requires imagination, planning such things as introducing animals, children and plants, plus gaining access to lush garden environments, and using the outside community more creatively.

Roles, rituals and routines also play an important part in the life of a person with dementia and there are some simple things that can be imaginatively included in the daily delivery of care by those who understand why it is important to make the most of every task encountered within the day. Ensuring variety is also important, as it provides stimulation and different challenges, which can break monotony and lift mood. So, a brief summary would be:

- Know as much about the person's past, their life story, interests, preferences and personality type as possible.
- Encourage the person to be spontaneous and express themselves, promoting liveliness and enjoyment.
- Give as many opportunities as possible for communicating, interacting and relating to others.

- Use more sensory and non-verbal ways of communicating in the later stages.
- Be flexible in choice of activity, and choose activities which you and the person with dementia can enjoy together.
- In activities, use your imagination and intuition, adopting a natural, joyful, humorous and playful approach.
- Successful approaches include verbal communication and visual stimulation.

PRESERVING COMMUNICATION

We have already seen that it is crucial we preserve the identity of the individual but, as we consider their ongoing wellbeing, it is also vital to preserve communication. Communication with people with dementia is possible and it's not just about talking; it is also about the use of facial expression, gesture, posture, touch, music, art. We need to be able to consider a range of issues, from the environment, to the individual's own way of seeing the world (style and preferences), and their preferred mode of communication. Often, it's useful to employ reminiscence as a conversation starter (childhood memories, important events, work); it is also important to remember practical considerations such as whether the person can see, or hear (for example, ensure glasses are clean). With a person with dementia, we need to get their attention before speaking – for instance, touching their arm – and get eye contact before talking. If possible, we should minimise distractions and background noise, and try to stimulate the senses.

When visiting someone with dementia, we must remember to avoid times of fatigue, such as after lunch or a tiring activity. It is helpful to identify ourselves, and address the person by their preferred name, speaking calmly and slowly, using short sentences, emphasising key words, using gestures, holding hands, and responding to the emotion behind their words. If a person forgets what they have just said, we can gently remind them of the subject being discussed. When they cannot seem to find the right words, we can help them: 'Do you mean chair or shoe?' or provide the first sound of the word: for example, 'p' for 'pen'. Word association can be useful: 'tooth ... brush, hair ... brush', as is using a combination of sound and lead-in cues: for example, 'you eat with a knife and f ...'.

CHALLENGES

At some point, challenges will need to be met and overcome. Any one of the following could become an issue.

1. Difficulty sleeping: carers should try to keep the person active during the day and prevent sleeping, keeping up physical exercise and walking, and ensuring the person is comfortable in bed at night.
2. Driving concerns: with dementia, judgment becomes impaired and reactions are slower. As normal driving is in the automatic movement memory, it can appear all right; however, dealing with the unexpected or getting lost will put the person and others at risk. Seek advice from the GP!
3. Repetitive behaviour: repetitive speech is common as the person forgets from one minute to the next. Make sure there is a time gap between questions, and reassure the person, rephrasing their words back to them; ensure needs have been met, provide distraction, offer something else to see, hear or do.
4. Clinging behaviour: this is often due to insecurity or inner fear of being abandoned, or bewilderment in an unfamiliar environment. This dependency can be exhausting and requires creativity: provide something to occupy the person

to allow the carer to do something else, or get a sitter, to allow some privacy and peace.

5. Losing things/accusations of theft: this can occur in the early stages of the illness and it is important not to get into a confrontation, as this can be related to deeper losses or previous experiences. Where did they last see the object? Do they have a favourite hiding place? Keep replacements of keys etc; check wastepaper baskets and bins before emptying them.

6. Hallucinations: the person may misinterpret what they see or hear, such as seeing a figure at the end of the bed, or people talking in the room. Try not to confront or contradict what they have seen or heard; instead, reassure them and use a calm and comforting voice and approach; distract attention to something real. If this symptom persists, see the GP as it may be due to certain medication. Something as simple as loss of eyesight and poor hearing can contribute to confusion – regular check ups are important.

7. Wandering: this may appear aimless, but it may not be to the person with dementia; however, it can be difficult for relatives to cope with, especially if the person gets lost. Safety must be a primary consideration, so make sure the person has some form of identification on them, and that there are systems in place so you know if they have gone outside. Keep an up-to-date photograph if you need to ask help from others. Never show anger when the person is found – restraining brings legal implications – also they will be unaware of what they have done. Be calm and reassuring.

8. Aggressive outbursts: find out what has triggered the situation; it is often due to loss of control or frustration in communication. Divert them to a calming activity. If violence occurs, seek professional help in managing this type of behaviour.

9. Difficulty retaining information and keeping up with familiar jobs/routines: gently take over related responsibilities as abilities diminish, and involve the person wherever possible, encouraging familiar, simple activities.

10. Unable to notice mistakes, solve problems or plan ahead: provide a structured routine, encouraging simple two- to three-step activities such as chores, dance/sport, board games or puzzles, remembering to help them when they become agitated and frustrated.

11. Unable to perform two- to three-step activities: reduce demand to one-step activities such as washing a car, sweeping, preparing vegetables. Find as many familiar simple tasks as you can and include them in conversation using uncomplicated sentences, using gestures and touch to communicate; encourage physical exercise.

12. Loss of motivation: this can be due to loss of confidence, interest or ability to initiate an activity. Give verbal prompts ('Can you help with me with …?') alongside physical prompts, such as handing the person the tool for the job, pointing and miming.

13. Poor communication: STOP, OBSERVE, LISTEN, ENGAGE – *observe* the person's mood, breathing, movement, *listen* to metaphor and words that may give clues to what they are trying to express, using the imagination; enter into their world, sharing common humanity rather than living 'on the other side'. Then *engage* with the emotion and need. Communicate using verbal and non-verbal methods.

MAINTAINING INDEPENDENCE

It may appear easier to overprotect the person with dementia, but this can lead to more challenges for both parties. Carers need to be patient, helping only when necessary. This takes some adjustment, but the most important thing is to give the person a meaningful role, and help them to stay as active as possible.

Try to organise an activity to provide a *sense of achievement.* Give assistance by finding things they can still do, however simple – such as peeling potatoes – rather than banishing them to a chair in front of the TV. There will be times when you will be surprised by how much they can do if the activity is one they formerly carried out routinely.

KEY POINTS TO REMEMBER

- The person's attention span will be short.
- Involve people in decisions using pictures and simple sentences if necessary.
- Walking or strolling (wandering) can happen for a range of reasons: to find a sense of meaning and familiarity; exercise to relieve stress or boredom.
- Provide a stimulating environment, using preferences and unexpected spontaneous 'happenings'.
- Emphasise the use of non-verbal communication such as gesture, matching their emotions, using touch, music.
- Everyday activities can be therapeutic (even for as short a time as thirty seconds).
- Consider the need for relaxation, light, massage, music and singing.
- Try not to focus an activity on the end result but on the process of 'doing' so that it is failure-free. Give simple instructions. Employ good communication using short 'key words'; start off an activity with the person, or do it with them to remind them.
- Enjoy old photographs, objects of significance and, in later

stages, explore different textures to feel and touch, closely monitoring the level of pleasure or anxiety when trying something new.

RESTOR8
EIGHT PRINCIPLES OF RESTORATION: RESTORING THE IMAGE OF THE PERSON

A very useful picture in regards to the 'restoration' of the image of the person with dementia comes from a personal family portrait belonging to my mother who had the Alzheimer's type of dementia, but had retained a high degree of wellbeing. She was a former picture restorer and art dealer from London. A half-restored painting is what she used to demonstrate the 'art and science of restoration'. It captures an occluded dark and distorted image (on half the canvas) which shows a full picture with all the hues of colour and form on the other side, as the former painting is revealed by careful application of restorative 'agents'. It is a pictorial and graphic visual impression of how the eight principles in RESTOR8 (a framework for people with dementia developed after twenty years of working in care homes and combining personal story and professional experience) could have the same effect of putting back into place what has been hidden. It is a classy image and has a ring of quality (use of classic art and culture) which offers a subliminal message.

My brother, Charles Brooking, the eminent architectural historian preserving and restoring the nation's heritage of buildings, and the owner and creator of the Brooking Collection, states:

> I am involved in turning back the clock by stripping away the effects of neglect. Giving the right treatment is essential in restoration work, taking off the degradation of years of over-painting and later additions, bringing it back to its original glory and halting further

decline. I celebrate the fact that objects can develop a depth and character with age.

Having worked in the 'people restoration' business in care homes with the very old and frail, the principles that work in this restorative, life-assisting approach are those chosen to inform RESTOR8 – eight principles to help restore people with dementia, using activity to raise wellbeing and promote ability-focused care. The key elements of the eight principles involved are:

- Activating
- Restoring
- Developing
- Communicating
- Enriching
- Releasing
- Empathising
- Connecting

For further details, see Appendix 2.

CONCLUSION

In this chapter, we have considered the wellbeing of the person with dementia. We have looked at the importance of activities, communication, maintaining skills, and some of the challenges involved. We have also considered points regarding maintaining independence, and looked at the principles of RESTOR8. In effect, it is all about relationships (see Appendix 3); helping the person experience home life in ways that generate and sustain their wellbeing and quality of life. The positive consequences of such care can give the person a feeling of security, continuity, belonging and a sense of purpose, fulfilment and significance.

Who they are and what they do *matters*, and they are valued. And, because dementia affects the person's ability to communicate effectively, we need to consider other ways to engage the person in meaningful stimulation, which enables them to truly 'connect'.

ACTIVITY

Think back to the piece above about a picture being restored. How has this helped or challenged you, as you think about the person you know and love who has dementia? If it helps, find an item – a picture, an ornament, material – that has faded or become damaged, and think about what it would take to restore it to its original glory. Put it somewhere where you will see it often, to remind you that you are part of the 'people restoration' business.

REFLECTION

Read through the Beatitudes, Matthew 5:3–10. How might each 'blessed' relate to the person with dementia, and those who care for them? Consider personalising the blessings: 'Blessed is (name of loved one), poor in spirit, for theirs is the kingdom of heaven. Blessed am I when I mourn for I shall be comforted …' etc.

PRAYER

Dear heavenly Father, may Your name be honoured. Thank You that you care so intimately about the detail of our lives. Help us to reflect Your care and concern so that we might become more like Jesus, who had time for all and esteemed all, for we are all Your unique creations and of infinite worth to You. Loving Creator, help us to help those whom You have created to know Your *shalom* of wellbeing. Amen.

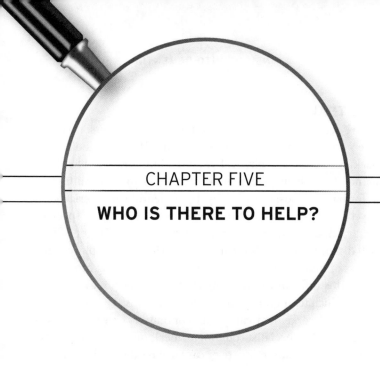

CHAPTER FIVE

WHO IS THERE TO HELP?

'So do not fear, for I am with you;
do not be dismayed, for I am your God.
I will strengthen you and help you;
I will uphold you with my righteous right hand.'
(Isaiah 41:10)

INTRODUCTION

So far, we have considered what dementia is, and looked at some of the issues involved in treatment and support. We have seen how important the maintenance of wellbeing is. But, especially as the dementia progresses, our loved one (and their carers) will need as much support as possible. It is important to know, therefore, both that there is a team of experts ready to help, and what assistance they can offer. In this chapter, we will look especially at the role of the occupational therapist.

THE TEAM

As we read in Chapter Two, the *GP* is the first person you are likely to visit for an initial assessment. They will look at the background, give a physical examination, and test blood and urine. The GP may then make a referral to a consultant for a formal diagnosis. This may be a neurologist, geriatrician, psychiatrist or psychologist, who will provide a specialist behavioural assessment. A brain scan, eg CAT, MRI or SPECT, will discover whether there has been shrinking, atrophy or areas of loss of function in the brain. However, the ageing process can make this difficult to differentiate. The specialist may prescribe drugs which temporarily relieve the symptoms.

A *social worker* may carry out a community care means tested assessment for specialist equipment, meals on wheels, home care, short respite breaks, day care or care in a residential home. He or she also can advise on benefits such as Attendance Allowance. Depending on the need, or specialist, *Admiral Nurses* (www.fordementia.org.uk) will take you through each stage of the illness and provide support for carers. Other nurses involved might be community psychiatric nurses (CPN), district nurses or health visitors. Further health professionals may include audiologists, dentists and optometrists. A *dietician* will advise on diet and nutrition, recommend ways to present food as well as helping those in the later stages when swallowing liquids becomes difficult. The local branch of the Alzheimer's Society is a good place to start looking for assistance, and provides a range of support to local sufferers and their families, from information through to day care.

A *specialist solicitor* (such as Solicitors for the Elderly) can advise on taking out Lasting Powers of Attorney under the Mental Capacity Act.

Access to rehabilitation professionals has not traditionally been available to people with dementia, many of whom would benefit from their expertise. A *physiotherapist* can help to improve physical activity, strength, balance and normal movement patterns, and provide advice to maximise mobility in different situations. Also, *speech and language therapists* and the *occupational therapist* have specific roles to offer. These professionals do not just focus on the physical aspects but the whole person – the physical, mental, emotional and social aspects (OR physically, mentally, emotionally and socially). This may focus on physical daily functional tasks, memory or communication difficulties

SPEECH AND LANGUAGE THERAPY
The speech and language therapist provides specialist assessment, analysis, diagnosis and management of communication disorders and associated swallowing problems, and as part of a multidisciplinary team works with carers and clients. They reduce the impact of the difficulty by providing advice, training and support if there is a clinical need for their involvement. In particular they can:

- Analyse language disorder to inform the diagnosis.
- Give a specialist assessment of eating and drinking and swallowing problems (dysphagia).
- Provide communication strategies to maintain and maximise function with specific management strategies.

OCCUPATIONAL THERAPY
Occupational therapy assists in providing encouragement, advice and support, helping carers to cope, using strategies to encourage activity, understanding the different levels of function,

encouraging positive behaviours and enabling the carer to draw the fine line between protecting their loved one, and their wider wellbeing. The therapist will help the carer aim for as normal a living arrangement as possible and accept the right to take normal living risks – and make mistakes.

Carer stress can be underestimated and is a significant contribution to the need for residential care. It is important that families and community carers are closely involved in discussions across and between the different agencies.

Occupational therapy can help with the following:

1. Functional tasks

These are complex. For example, the maintaining of continence, where a person must be able to know where to go (orientation, recognition), be able to get there (mobility and safety), and be able to 'hold on' until they do so (awareness, memory of distance, judgment, mobility, sphincter control – that is, controlling their urge to urinate). It's important to consider the side-effects of medication and other health conditions that may be present. Therapists can advise and support carers to help adapt the environment and provide a meaningful day for the person with dementia through the right selection and application of daily living tasks and occupations.

2. Memory strategies, eg diaries

These help to give a sense of control, reducing anxiety. These strategies might involve the writing down of significant actions, and looking back, in diaries. People with dementia need routine and orientation props such as lists, labels, journals.

3. Group work

Physical and social activities can encourage a sense of competitiveness, motivation, enjoyment and laughter. Attendance at day centres or group rehabilitation facilities can be helpful for some people, depending on their level of impairment.

4. Home

Different tasks can be broken down into stages, to enable a sense of achievement; for instance, laying a table with an adequate amount of props (for example, a written list or diagram of what goes where).

5. Safety

The occupational therapist will help the carer to consider chair height, firmness, colour contrast, elimination of floor clutter, rugs and so on. Many accidents happen in the kitchen!

6. Falls risk

Considering cognitive, physical and psychological effects, the therapist can issue appropriate guidelines to promote mobility.

7. Meaningful activity

They will also be able to provide an assessment to determine what type of activities could be carried out to improve health, and how to employ these for maximum benefit. Although it is difficult to distinguish between each stage of dementia, the model on the next page outlines four ability levels and demonstrates the shrinking and changing world at each progression.[1] (See Appendix 4.)

Stage of dementia	Developmental stage	Potential activities
Early dementia	Reflective (Planned: PAL)	Games, physical competitive games/ sports, quizzes, discussions, end-product tasks, structured crafts, work-type activity
Early to middle dementia	Symbolic (Exploratory: PAL)	Music, dance, drama, art, poetry, reminiscence, story telling, festive/ seasonal and spiritual activities
Middle to late dementia	Sensorimotor (Sensory: PAL)	Movement, massage, cooking, stacking, rummaging, dolls and soft toys, balls, exercise, bubbles, balloons, gardening, folding, polishing, wiping, sweeping, 'clowning'
Late dementia	Reflex (Reflex: PAL)	Singing, rocking, holding, non-verbal communication, smiling, stroking. Reflex responses to direct stimulation

FURTHER SUGGESTIONS

People with dementia can have difficulties interpreting their surroundings, misinterpreting the use of equipment; they can neglect part of their body, unable to see things due to altered perception of the environment, and may have problems recognising objects and what they are used for. An occupational therapist can help with advice on daily living support.

Consider the following:[2]

Clothing	• Use Velcro to replace buttons etc • Keep clothing simple, avoid complicated fastenings • Lay clothes out in the order they are to be put on. Use repetition
Eating	• There may be difficulties in remembering the last meal, checking whether food is hot/cold, holding cutlery, chewing and swallowing • Use reminders, finger food; serve one portion at a time, small/appetising. Enjoy cooking together as long as possible • Ensure contrasts such as a different coloured plate against a tablecloth background • Specialist cutlery may help if there are additional problems, eg padded cutlery • Special beakers or drinking straws • Swallowing difficulties – thickeners to put into drinks; here, consult speech and language therapist

Falling	• Remove loose mats, keep rooms uncluttered • Encourage person to pick up feet and take longer strides. Ensure feet are well looked after (nails, corns, calluses) • Wear supporting (not too tight) shoes with low heels and non-slip soles • Slippers can encourage a shuffling walk • Don't pull/push individual • Patterned carpets can cause confusion • Depth of stairs – mark edges with bright masking tape to help person to see the edge (contrast) • Dimmer switch/night light to assist orientation and reduce anxiety
Mobility	• To encourage use of grab rails near toilet seats to encourage better independence and assist difficulties getting on/off seat • Raise armchairs on special blocks of suitable height. If a walking aid is used, ensure ferrules (rubber ends) are in good repair and nuts and screws not loose. • GP referral to community physiotherapist for advice

Bathing/ personal hygiene	• GP to refer to occupational therapist for advice on type of support to suit individual needs
	• Maintain routine, try to make this a relaxing and pleasant occasion. Shower may be easier than bath
	• Simplify task as much as possible. If a person refuses to wash, try later. Consider dignity and modesty, covering up parts if embarrassed. Create routine for using WC, label or keep door open so it is easy to locate, limit drinks before bed and use commode by bed if necessary. See continence nurse via GP for advice or occupational therapist for equipment

MAINTAINING ABILITIES IN EVERYDAY LIFE

Bathing and washing: The occupational therapist will work with preferred ways and routines of doing things as 'old habits die hard', establishing the level of help really needed. Over-care can prevent someone from using their ablilities (or capabilities) however limited these are, so that they lose confidence and become even more dependent. We should always consider privacy and dignity, thinking about how we would feel in the same situation.

Toilet and continence: The therapist will advise the carer to ensure the person recognises the room, using a picture or sign if necessary; clothes need to be easy to manage (for example, elastic waists). Moist tissues are a helpful addition to have to hand; carers should try to establish a routine and watch for signs of discomfort.

Dressing: Carers need to allow enough time for the person with dementia to get dressed, providing guidance or assistance if needed. In this, limited and simple choices should be offered, such as 'Would you like the white shirt or the blue one?' rather than 'What would you like to wear?' It might help to lay the clothes out in order, starting with underwear on top of the pile, or handing out each garment one at a time, using short instructions, demonstrating what to do; even doing it together can be very effective. Use of labels, pictures, or storing whole outfits together provides simple choices. Too much clutter and choice is confusing for most of us!

Hair care and grooming: The carer needs to always explain what is going on and ensure eye contact is made before doing any of these personal care-type activities. Carers need to try to encourage choice and enjoyment of the sensory experience of touch when using hair and hand care. Hand massage and nail care can be pleasant and relaxing.

SENSORY APPROACH

Sensory stimulation is needed for people in later stages of dementia to help them to relate to the environment and other people. Sensory impairment and deprivation can affect this interaction process. Sensory stimulation is a direct approach using a range of stimuli to heighten awareness of the environment.[3] These can be presented as smell, movement, touch, vision, hearing and taste. It has the benefit of prompting familiar functional behaviour, providing pleasure and reassurance and an opportunity for stimulating emotional expression by providing reassuring, orientating information. Consider the wealth of natural seasonal and sensory-rich material. Familiar objects can be used, such as a pair of red mittens (colour, texture, putting-on, naming, recollection of wearing).

The greater the level of impairment the smaller the physical environment becomes to the person with dementia. As it shrinks, the attentive presence of a carer can improve wellbeing by getting the greatest emotional closeness possible using good eye contact and a sense of playfulness. This enables the carer to enter the person's 'bubble', or their small world. Every communication is an *opportunity* to enhance orientation, encourage reminiscence and communication, and promote individual identity and self-worth. Here are some ideas.

Seeing: Large pictures/colour prints; photographs.

Smelling: Herbs, plants; everyday aromas of cooking and household, eg polish.

Touching: Feet in water, sand; objects from nature/countryside, all to evoke memories; sensory blankets, cushions, objects with qualities of rough/smooth, hot/cold, massage/touch-based therapies.

Hearing: Music to stimulate memory, relax, energise or to remember with/sing along to; verses/poetry; garden sounds.

Tasting: Different food, sweets, savouries, jams, chutneys, tastes from the past; hot and cold drinks.

Moving: Cleaning, dusting, sorting, washing, moving to sound/music; outdoors – walking, hanging out washing, gardening.

WHEN THE GOING GETS TOUGH

In a person with dementia, behaviour we find difficult can be an attempt at communication. So we need to stop, observe and listen, identifying feelings behind the behaviour and trying guesswork from our knowledge of the person. A correct guess can reduce stress and improve satisfaction. Always ask what a person is trying to communicate. Trying to see the world from their angle is the secret to overcoming and preventing difficult situations arising.

It is helpful to see what triggers this behaviour, what time of day it occurs and whether there is a pattern which might relate to past activities, such as going for a walk with the dog or collecting children from school etc. We all have good and bad days!

Consider the need for security, comfort, occupation, a particular role, or to be loved and included, and to have purpose; these may all contribute to a person's behaviour in trying to meet their needs in that moment. An empathetic response is helpful, where feelings can be expressed and acknowledged; listening is important, as is providing roles that can be devised to meet emotional or occupational needs.

Interpreting behaviour requires considerable patience on the part of the carer. Remember not to take aggression personally as it may be a result of frustration, pain or discomfort, of being startled, frightened or confused. People with dementia cannot problem-solve or learn from their experience.

'Positive person work' is about communication styles which have a positive, restorative effect on relationships. This approach originated from Tom Kitwood and is closely linked to counselling techniques. They include methods that reduce the likelihood of behaviour which is challenging to us, such as:

- Recognition: having an open attitude without prejudice, respecting uniqueness of individuals.
- Negotiation: asking, consulting and listening without preconceived ideas about what is needed.
- Collaboration: not imposing power through coercion, but rather facilitating a contribution.
- Playfulness: engaging in spontaneity, humour and joyfulness.
- Sensory stimulation.
- Celebration: thankfulness and appreciation of what is.

- Relaxation: a calm, unhurried approach that allows people to do things at their own pace.
- Validation: accepting the reality of feelings from the other person's perspective.
- Holding: remaining fully present and responsive to the other person.
- Facilitation: enabling, making it easier for the person.
- Giving: celebrating the giving of the other. [4]

It is also helpful to maintain a predictable routine and to avoid activities involving crowds and confusing stimuli. We need to be aware, too, of the importance of the use of touch and tone of voice, and to consider concentration span, and frustration levels.

CONCLUSION

It is vital for the carer to see that they are not 'alone' in caring for the person with dementia. There is help available, which can enrich and enhance the life of the person being cared for, as well as giving much-needed support, assistance, guidance and relief to the carer. It is conducive, therefore, to the wellbeing of both parties that there should be a full exploration of what's on offer – taking note particularly of the role of the occupational therapist, whose skills can be invaluable in the often difficult journey being travelled with the loved one.

ACTIVITY

Remember, using the senses is important for people who now depend on them to make sense of their world. Look again at the ideas for a sensory approach on page 77. If you made a Memory Box (see Chapter Three), consider how you could use personal, 'sensory' artefacts to aid helpful reminiscence, such as photographs, perfume, textured cloth such as silk or wool. Try to include music; music and singing are particularly powerful, for they make many links in the brain which have the potential to encourage a sense of wellbeing.

REFLECTION

Caring for someone with dementia can be extremely tiring, as well as rewarding. It's important to take care of ourselves, as well as the person for whom we care. Reflect on the fact that Jesus tells us to cast our cares on Him (1 Pet. 5:7) – He does not expect us to bear the burden alone. Can you cast your care on Him today? If you find it too hard, ask a close friend to pray with you; share your concerns and prayer requests regularly with a trusted friend or church leader, if you are able.

PRAYER

Lord Jesus, You were often tired and weary. As well as being Almighty God, You were human, just as we are. Lord, thank You that You are willing to bear our burdens. Thank You that You say, 'My grace is sufficient for you, for my power is made perfect in weakness' (2 Cor. 12:9). Help us today to trust in Your perfect power, Your amazing grace, and Your unconditional love. Amen.

CHAPTER SIX

CARE OPTIONS[1]

'God is our refuge and strength,
an ever-present help in trouble.'
(Psalm 46:1)

INTRODUCTION

It's important to find the best care option for the loved one with dementia, and for the carer, and it is good to discuss this with the person who needs care, at the earliest stage. Talking about what to do means family members know the wishes of the person concerned, even if it is not always possible or practical to carry them out.

Care choices can range from short-stay respite care to provide a break for the carer, to moving the person with dementia into a care home, which has advantages and disadvantages, as we will discover. Choosing the right care home is important, and a decision often made at crisis point. Whilst the carer can feel guilt or a sense of failure, for many it's a positive option and a good solution for all concerned.

In this chapter, we will take an objective view of care available, so we can make informed choices when we need to.

PREPARING FOR CHANGE

To encourage a realistic view of the situation, plus encouraging relatives to consider the wider impact for all concerned, the issue of care can be raised as a family problem rather than just an individual one. It's important to understand emotional issues when someone is faced with the challenge of relinquishing their independence and the things that matter to them. The feeling of being in control can be easily lost in the middle of an emergency situation, and this can have a devastating effect on the person's wellbeing and sense of security, continuity – and self-worth.

Discussions with the loved one will need great sensitivity; if they have communication difficulties, remember to speak slowly and clearly, being patient and allowing time for the person to take in and respond to information. It may be easier to focus on the specific needs arising from their condition or disability, with its long-term implications, rather than the ultimate solution.

Carers need to make decisions about the timing regarding making a change in care. For example:

- What has changed in the last six months?
- What did the person with dementia manage to do last year that they cannot do now?
- Are they realistic about what they are able to do?
- Are they a risk to themselves and to others?
- How important is it to their wellbeing to be surrounded by people, or have access to other people when they need it?

EMERGENCY

Although planning ahead is a good idea, emergency planning may take effect if a person suffers a sudden or serious illness which leaves them dependent on 24-hour care. Or, it may be that the carer is not able to continue caring due to health problems or stress. (The problem of dealing with incontinence can be a trigger to difficulties in coping.) A carer may be reluctant to relinquish their role; an outside professional such as a GP may need to give the carer 'permission' to let go. The maintenance of the relationship may be the most important thing to consider in this instance; being pushed beyond the ability to cope can have disastrous effects on relationships.

PRESERVING RELATIONSHIPS

There will be many emotions a carer might experience – we looked at some of these on page 37. Everyone finds different aspects of this experience challenging, and families must strive to keep communication channels open. The stress of caring necessitates a series of coping strategies. These can include talking and sharing with a trusted friend, church or family member, pursuing interests and hobbies, listening to inspiring music, and taking one day at a time.

CARE CHOICES

- A *short-stay respite care* in a local care home to provide a break for a carer.
- A period of *short-term rehabilitation* for an older person to maintain independence for longer (also assisting the carer).
- *Intermediate care* is available in some areas; a minority of care homes provide this service.
- The person with dementia could *move near to, or live with, their*

family, enabling the family to regularly provide or supervise the help they need.

- They could *move to a sheltered housing scheme* with access to additional support.
- *Assistive technology* can help some people remain in their own homes for longer. Introducing technology can make the environment safer. Sensors with alarms and other equipment can aid independence in daily living and personal care. Tasks such as getting in and out of a bath safely can be assessed by a local authority or an independent occupational therapist. Additional support from an agency might enable someone to stay in their home, or there could be a greater care package where necessary.
- *Home care.* If the person's relatives feel able to provide care for the person at home, they should ensure that adequate community nursing and other forms of support are available. Getting an assessment from social services is a good start to finding out what is available locally. Personal budgets are now available and may be a workable option for some people. Home carers assist with the activities of daily living; for example, getting up, going to bed, dressing, toileting, personal hygiene, and will be trained in manual handling, using hoists and so on. They may have additional training in mental health and dementia care.
- *Care homes.* Some care homes are prepared to care for people with dementia at the end of their lives. But some interventions that are available in a hospital (see below) may not be available in a care home. Some couples choose to move into a home together.
- *Hospital.* Most people with dementia admitted to hospital during the final stages are actually admitted because of another illness. It is important to make sure that hospital staff are aware

that the person has dementia. It is also helpful to ensure they are informed of any particular communication, emotional, psychological or physical needs and preferences of a relative to inform their care plans and prevent as far as possible any misunderstandings or distress. Hospital chaplains are also available as a valuable source of comfort and support.

- *Hospices.* Hospices offer palliative care when the illness is no longer treatable. Palliative care focuses on reducing physical and psychological distress, and provides support to the family. Most people in the late stages of dementia require good nursing care, which can be provided in nursing homes or at the person's own home by the district nursing team. A few have rather more complex symptoms or other problems which may benefit from specialist input from palliative home care services or hospices.

CARE HOMES
ADVANTAGES

- The continuity of care and the security of being able to get help when needed may relieve anxiety. Otherwise, people with dementia might be dependent on domiciliary visits which can be erratic, creating insecurity.
- Quality of life may be seen to go down by moving into a care home, but many people settle well, adapt, and enjoy the security and support in their new way of living.
- No responsibility for running and maintaining a home. They will no longer need to shop and cook meals – which can be a real struggle, particularly at a point in life when getting the nutrition necessary to stay well physically and mentally is crucial.
- The burden of care is reduced. For some relatives, being unburdened from exhausting care in the home can help them to rekindle former aspects of their relationship.

- Having time to try new activities may be a bonus for some people. Previous life may have been determined by having just enough energy to do the basic chores.
- Companionship opportunities: new friendships can be made. Sharing with others helps to prevent loneliness and isolation, and provides an opportunity for new relationships to blossom. Good care homes help residents get to know each other and build a sense of community.
- They provide opportunities for 'inter-dependence' within a caring community.
- There can be more flexibility and choice as to when care is delivered during the day.

DISADVANTAGES
- Losing the independence of running one's own home is particularly difficult for some people, especially when it is closely associated with their identity.
- It can mean a loss of freedom and decision-making control. Some enjoy having their own routine, or like to live a more flexible lifestyle. However, many good homes work hard to provide flexible care to suit individual preferences. Loss of familiar surroundings can make a person feel insecure and dependent.
- Personal space may be limited, and having to adjust to life in a community is more challenging for some people than others. Those who like a lot of space and to have their furniture and possessions around them may struggle with living in more confined circumstances.
- Some may resent the legal status of being in a care home. They may view it as less than being a tenant in rented accommodation, living under the terms of the contract agreed. There may be concerns about how this contract could be threatened if at some

stage the finances ran out and the person was subsequently made homeless, or would require 'top up' fees from another source; this may cause an additional burden on relatives.

- Having to move into a home and the accompanying resettling may be very difficult. Some people who feel pressured into moving can have problems adapting to the idea; they may even feel 'dumped' by their family.[2]

MAKING THE DECISION

Once relatives have made the decision that a care home is the best option for their loved one, mixed feelings can occur, including guilt. However, although the media highlights and uncovers negative stories, there are many people living in care homes who have fulfilling lives, supported by dedicated staff. We do not often hear these stories, or read about those who struggle on in their own homes, often suffering emotional neglect, insecurity and loneliness. The right care home can open up new possibilities and ensure that frail older people with complex needs have a good quality of life.

TYPES OF HOMES AVAILABLE

Care homes either provide 'personal care' (residential homes) or 'nursing care' (nursing homes). They can be run for profit, or by charities or other non-profit making organisations, and vary in size as well as emphasis. Some homes, for example, cater for religious groups, or have a particular ethos.

THE ENVIRONMENT

Care homes vary in size; some buildings may have been converted or adapted; some are purpose-built. It is important to consider what the relative will require in terms of environment, facilities and so on. Also, the location and situation of the home in meeting the needs of the person and those visiting them should be considered.

QUALITY IN MANAGEMENT AND STAFF

A good home should have an open style of leadership, with a quality improvement system which is central to a home's staff development and operational management. A person-centred home activated by personal relationships is one which involves management, residents, staff and family members in quality initiatives. Successful homes should strive to continually improve, learn and develop practice.

CARE PLANS

Care plans are key documents containing guidance which will inform the care and quality of life that the person with dementia will receive. Relatives can be involved in care planning if the person wants this and it is in their best interests. The information the relative can supply is very important; we need to make sure the home knows what makes our loved one anxious, what things make them feel upset or angry, what they enjoy, how they like to pass the time, about any significant close relationships and how one can tell when the person is upset, or content. Abilities should be expressed in a positive way, highlighting individual needs.[3]

ETHOS OF THE HOME

- A person-centred community strives to preserve individual choice and identity, which involves residents as partners in care planning and community decision-making.
- Preserving individuality is an essential part of a good care home and can be expressed in quality care planning informed by life biography, taking into consideration abilities, preferences in daily living activities, previous lifestyle and personality type.

- The practice of good care will be enabling and nurturing with an emphasis on wellbeing, mutuality and interdependence between all parties, ie residents, staff, relatives (the relationship triangle) and management. Work should be organised with clearly defined roles and responsibilities, encouraging positive relationships and communication, helping residents to know who is in charge of them. Staff relationships should be collegiate, with leadership supporting practice development; team work should be demonstrated by the level of involvement of all the groups in decision-making. Stable and fulfilled staff should feel they are equipped and valued by their managers, and be able to deliver good care.[4]

MAINTAINING QUALITY OF LIFE

This means different things to different people, but positive relationships between residents, relatives and staff, involvement in care planning, community life and having access to meaningful activities, are particularly important. Having care delivered at a dignified pace, including time to listen to residents about what matters to them, all contribute to a good quality experience.

Here are some key questions based on what matters to residents in care homes (adapted from part of The Resident Centred Care Home Standard™. This is a practice development, quality improvement and relationship/person-centred outcome tool developed by Rosemary Hurtley and Pat Duff OBE for care homes).

1. Do residents have control over decisions about personal care, as far as they are able?
2. Are there opportunities for social/occupational activity where residents are able to take part in meaningful, spontaneous and planned activities? Do these have relevance with their interests

and capabilities, and are they integrated into the care plans supported by staff with specifically assigned responsibilities?

3. How are residents supported to have choice and influence in the food/menus, and given the right level of practical help during meal times?

4. Is spiritual and religious support available to help residents find meaning and follow important practices in acceptable ways, and can they feel confident about receiving the best end of life care that respects individual wishes?

5. How are concerns and complaints responsively and openly dealt with regarding any aspect of home life raised by relatives or residents?

Visiting relatives appreciate a home where their roles are recognised and they are treated with understanding by staff and managers, demonstrated by the welcoming atmosphere, quality and extent of information and communication systems, as well as how they are supported to contribute in different ways.

SUMMING UP

It's true to say that people with dementia are at risk of developing psychological and behavioural symptoms such as agitation and disturbed moods. They are at greater risk of becoming confused if physical health needs are not addressed quickly. Depression is frequently undiagnosed. It's important, within a care home, to find out the perspectives of the person, and to promote the building of relationships and engagement with others. Improving practice must focus on well-trained carers and helping people to live to the full. Good care plans should be clearly written, accessible, and draw on life experiences. They should be drawn up with the person living in the home and their carers, if the resident wishes this. The staff should ensure the individual's choices are put into practice. A care home must look at the whole person, addressing health, personal, social and emotional needs. There must be clear instructions for staff about how to address requirements in an ability-focused way. Staff need more awareness about all areas of care and wellbeing and should be encouraged to read the care plan.

Withdrawn, disengaged behaviour may indicate a lack of appropriate stimulation and a poor culture of care. Many approaches are too task-orientated and do not pay attention to the quality of communication, verbal and non-verbal, which has a great bearing on how people with dementia feel. It can be easier for staff to let people sleep for inappropriately long periods during the day, due to boredom, lack of stimulation and nothing else to do; having a conversation and constructive engagement has a positive effect on mood. Non-verbal ways of showing social/emotional language is vital.

Keeping in touch with people who are important to the person should be encouraged by involving the relatives, and care homes need to understand their feelings of stress and anxiety, and make them welcome.

It's helpful to consider the following in the process of choosing a home for a loved one:

- General state of observable emotional wellbeing of residents.
- Level of engagement with people (staff, visitors and others) in a task or activity (eating, walking, observing, looking at a magazine), or with an object.
- Style of interaction and communication with people living in the home: positive – warm, supportive, friendly and caring approaches; neutral – task-orientated questions such as, 'Do you want a drink?'; negative – cold, disrespectful comments that undermine wellbeing or treat a person like a child.

Also:

- Does the manager seem friendly and approachable?
- How open is management to suggestions and involvement from the family?
- Is the care organised in person-centred ways, with particular staff taking responsibility for a specific resident's wellbeing? And is the staffing based on the needs of residents?

END OF LIFE
THE 'LONG BEREAVEMENT' OF DEMENTIA

When a person has dementia, from the earliest time you notice changes in them, right until the end, you may feel you are gradually saying goodbye to them. Some people even say, 'She isn't my sister anymore' or 'He's not the person I married' or 'She is just the shadow of who she was'. The experience of supporting someone through their dementia, marked by stages of loss and sadness along the way, has been described as a 'long bereavement'. Being aware of your own reactions to grief and its origins can help you to cope. In recognising that you are entering a period of painful change and loss and its accompanying deep emotions, you will be able to take care of yourself and accept your feelings for what they are.

It's helpful to plan for the final days and, if you can, to talk with your loved one well in advance about their hopes and fears about the end of life. Many people in the final stages of dementia live in a care home, although some may be in hospital and a few may still live at home. End of life wishes need to be discussed and incorporated into care plans, and all health and social care staff involved will be trained, both in the community and in care homes, to deal openly with this issue, using good communication and respecting choices as far as possible.

PALLIATIVE CARE

Palliative care is a philosophical approach where there is no cure at the end of life. It neither tries to lengthen nor shorten life, but rather to maintain the physical, psychological and spiritual comfort of the individual until death.

If someone in the later stages of dementia becomes seriously ill, there may be a discussion about whether to try to prolong their life or to allow them to die naturally. Interventions may include resuscitation after a heart attack, antibiotic treatment for pneumonia, or giving the person foods or liquids other than by mouth. Resuscitation may be unsuccessful in people in the final stages of dementia, and even when it is successful, there is a risk of causing further brain damage. Only the doctor can make the final decision about whether to give or withhold treatment at this point. However, the views of relatives and of the person with dementia should always be taken into account where possible.

The life expectancy of a person with dementia is unpredictable, and the disease can progress for up to around ten to twelve years. Although dementia is a life-shortening illness, another condition or illness (such as bronchopneumonia) may cause death, and be given as reason for death on the death certificate. The person's ability to cope with infections and other physical problems will be impaired due to the progress of the condition, and the person may die because of a clot on the lung or a heart attack. However, in some people no specific cause of death is found, other than dementia. If the person is over seventy, ageing may also be given as a contributory factor.[5]

BEING PREPARED

Under the new Mental Capacity Act, people are strongly encouraged to write an advance decision (previously known as a living will or advanced directive), setting out the types of interventions they would not want doctors to provide at the end of their life. This is particularly important, as it means that people in the early stages of dementia have the opportunity to shape and make choices about any palliative care that they may need as the illness progresses.

CONCLUSION

Carers need a listening ear, time out for themselves, and to keep in touch with the outside world. They need someone to help them through the maze of information and services, benefits and professionals, plus sufficient information in regards to the next step. Thinking about and then choosing a care home can be very stressful, as is facing the long bereavement of dementia.

Having explored other options and decided that the time is right and a care home is the best choice, or compromise, getting the best 'fit' requires knowing what is important for the person concerned, considering their personality, previous lifestyle, interests and abilities. Every situation is unique, and there will be pros and cons. What is right for one person and their circumstances will vary including health, carer stress, or specific environment needs. The unknown is often laced with uncertainty or anxiety, but many will acknowledge how it can be a positive, even enjoyable solution for all.

ACTIVITY

Spend some time examining any areas where you feel you would appreciate further support. What help do you require? Contact your local Alzheimer's Society branch. They will always be willing to talk to you and offer advice and information to support you. Talk to your church leadership or pastoral care group. Don't be reticent in asking for prayer, company or any practical assistance you might need.

REFLECTION

Matthew 5:4 says: 'Blessed are those who mourn, for they will be comforted.' And we see in John 11:35 that Jesus felt grief. We also read in Luke 7:13 how Jesus felt when He saw a bereaved widow – 'his heart went out to her and he said, "Don't cry."' Be assured that Jesus knows what you are going through. Ask Him to put His comforting arms around you, and spend some time reflecting on the fact that He knows, He cares, and you are loved.

PRAYER

Lord Jesus, thank You that You are with us every step of the way, even though the journey is tough. We may ask 'Why?' but You just ask us to trust You and assure us that You are in the situation with us. Fill us with Your Holy Spirit; give us wisdom to make the right decisions, for we need Your guidance. Lord, may we feel Your gracious presence and Your peace today. Amen.

CHAPTER SEVEN

SPIRITUAL CARE

'Are your wonders known in the place of darkness,
or your righteous deeds in the land of oblivion?'
(Psalm 88:12)

INTRODUCTION

If you are over sixty-five years old and living in the UK, you are likely to have had some attachment to a church. The Church in general often fails to pay sufficient attention to the needs of the growing numbers of over eighty-fives, who are often not prepared for drastic life changes or the loss of control which may arise from giving – or being on the receiving end of – care. People need active help to remain in the 'mainstream' of life; this is a tall order for a society wedded to ideals of individualism over community. Sadly, the western Church often reflects society's values – and ageism.

But a sense of 'belonging' can help to support loss and bereavements experienced in later life.

The process of dementia moves people from a place of 'doing' to one of 'being', and with this, a risk of losing unique individual identity can follow in its wake, unless efforts are made to support closeness to God through more visual and tangible closeness.[1] It is important therefore for the person to find meaning and purpose, experience intimacy to prevent loneliness, have hope, and be able to cope with uncertainty as they move from 'doing' to 'being'.

THE VALUE OF SPIRITUAL LIFE

It is vital for wellbeing that spiritual requirements be considered when caring for those with dementia, providing opportunities to give and receive, such as being helpful and feeling useful to another, providing a sense of service, hope for the future, faith, peace and security. Any religious needs (worship, prayer, Scripture and meditation) should also be met. It is acknowledged that having a faith is a big factor in helping people cope with life's changes and challenges.

The inability to get out, the breakdown of social networks, depression (closely linked with dementia), major life-change, malnutrition, disability and falls, contribute to people feeling less bothered with the outer things at the end of life than they are with relationships. But faith is still important, and rituals such as daily prayers, hymns, songs and habitual practices help people to remain spiritually connected, valued and aware.

HELPING PEOPLE RELATE TO GOD

When relating to God, we can display a spirit of thankfulness, appreciation, joy in the little things, living in the moment, using creativity, the arts, music and song, hymns and recitations previously learnt by heart. We need to help people with dementia to use their spiritual coping patterns, nurturing, in the early stages, the source of meaning (personal faith). When helping the person with dementia relate to God, you might like to look at this spiritual checklist.

- Is the person at peace with themselves?
- How do they normally express their faith/belief in God, and what support do they need to be able to continue this (eg church attendance, favourite music, hymns, programmes, important visitors)?
- In what ways do current difficulties affect their ability to continue to connect with God and others in familiar ways?
- What matters most to them in their life now, and makes them feel happy, lifts their spirit or touches their emotions?
- What hopes, fears or dreams do they have?
- What type of support is needed to remain connected with God in meaningful ways?
- How do they normally cope in situations that are stressful?
- Does the person seem content in themselves most of the time? Do they appear sad, unhappy most of the time?
- Do they feel life is worth living?
- What are the things that motivate them?

There could be pastoral needs, especially if a person experiences fear of death, non-fulfilment in life, depression, or has difficulties coping with dependency.[2]

SPIRITUAL CARE IN CARE HOMES
Managers and staff should be aware of the importance religion plays in a person's life, and encourage them to continue to express their belief in familiar customs and practices.

Extra care should be exercised when listening to matters which deeply concern them.

FRAMEWORK FOR ASSESSING SPIRITUAL NEEDS

As well as checking a person's general health, and their emotional wellbeing, the following need to be assessed:

- A person's concept of themselves.
- Their perception of what is happening to them.
- Hopes, fears and natural support mechanisms.
- The strength and nature of support from family and friends.
- The nature of relationships.
- Own views and beliefs in relation to their situation.
- Religious and cultural background.
- Life experience.
- Coping mechanisms.
- How open they are to receiving help.

SOME PRINCIPLES OF DELIVERING SPIRITUAL CARE

Allow time for solitude, quiet, creative sharing of gifts, the arts; recognise likes/dislikes, beliefs, values and how a person connects with other people. It is important to offer warm human befriending relationships, walking alongside at the pace of the individual, and to recognise inherent drive towards growth (people can grow despite their limitations), using encouragement and motivation, providing opportunities to recall and reflect on life experiences. We need to recognise the themes and symbols important to cultures, helping individuals to reconnect with faith and worship, and follow customary practices. Support, empathise, acknowledge and affirm frailty; recognise and acknowledge pain. Promote healthy living, signposting to specialists – eg pastoral support – where needed. Provide opportunity to give and receive, listen to stories and encourage reflection, and develop a sense of shared community, enjoying closeness to others (friendship, support and encouragement).

TAKING A SERVICE FOR PEOPLE WITH DEMENTIA

Meaning for people with dementia is synonymous with relationship. Despite the erosion of memory, therefore, aim to use opportunities for deep connection.[3] A service provides a sense of community in the present moment, sharing common beliefs, values, traditions and interests, and provides a sense of continuity and security for people with dementia through relationships and sharing together.

In thinking about taking a service for people with dementia, consider the time of day; late morning is best. Avoid early afternoons, or early evening for some. Create an intimate feel using chairs in a circular arrangement, with comfortable seating, access to sockets and enough room to manoeuvre wheelchairs. It is important to have a room which is not constantly interrupted, to prevent distraction. It can be helpful to stimulate the senses and include music; above all, do not make the encounter an intellectual experience. Also, be aware people might need assistance in working through feelings that may be triggered by memories. Wherever possible, invite friends and family to share the worship.

Here are some helpful tips:

- Arrive ten to fifteen minutes before the service to meet people and set up the service if it is in a care home (or day centre).
- Keep the service short (fifteen to twenty minutes), ensuring that it is planned in advance, but allows enough flexibility to provide prompts at a pace that is not too fast to follow. Corporate worship helps to reconnect with faith heritage and assists people to connect with meaningfulness. It gives an opportunity to involve local churches that have different patterns of faith practice/traditions, which provide memory anchors and cues.

But be encouraged to try novel ideas and ways of presenting them.

- Introduce yourself to each person at eye level, not towering over them, particularly at the beginning and end of worship. Minister with calmness, patience and gentleness; remember their humanity is still intact.
- Forming relationships and friendships is more important than evoking conversation, affirming the individual as special in God's sight.
- Introduce the act of worship by saying the time of day, commenting on weather and time of year, welcoming people.
- Demonstrate interest in individuals with good eye contact – don't be discouraged if people are distracted; sometimes using a picture or an object can be helpful.
- Sharing a group activity can create a sense of community (decorating a Christmas tree, for example).
- Use as many visual cues as possible, such as a white cloth, a cross, flowers on the table and suitable attire, depending on tradition.
- Use short and simple sentences and avoid theological jargon.
- Use large-print hymns and choruses; if an order of service is used, make sure there are clear headings and pictures to amplify the text.
- Have clear beginnings and endings, eg light a candle or use words such as 'We meet in the name of the Living God' and use a familiar blessing at the end.
- Use touch to engage people, helping them to gently connect with here and now – pay attention to those who cry out for help; this is often due to fear or the unfamiliarity of the environment.
- Try to love unconditionally and offer comfort as a form of healing for those with memory loss.
- Use touch, taste and smell sensitively as communication aids.

- Be prepared to repeat things, and say it in a different, simple way.
- Allow enough time for people to respond to questions, visual aids and body language.
- Use a range of arts sources to enrich, such as poetry, drama, dance.
- Move around the group smoothly, and never shout or startle people, always observing feelings and emotions closely.
- Have other support present to help with gaining responses, such as help with singing or following a passage.
- Use familiar and well-loved hymns, songs (perhaps from Sunday school days) and passages which link into long-term memory, and incorporate some reminiscence about the past. Try to use those with a strong sense of rhythm and regular pattern, keeping a good volume.
- Prayer: include intercession, thanksgiving, litany, bidding and silence; employ helpful symbols such as candles, pebbles or a cross.
- Keep reading of passages short, using those that stress God's presence, love and forgiveness rather than 'sin and guilt'.
- Use corporate confession emphasising forgiveness – such as use of the Lord's Prayer. The reciting of familiar, previously learnt prayers can remain intact in the person with dementia, even though other forms of communication may be lost.
- A short talk rather than a sermon must be simple and illustrated with props and visual and tactile aids where possible, but not presented in a childish or patronising way.
- Try to provide 'helping' roles for people to feel valued and useful, and part of the activity.
- Try to give a personalised blessing: 'God bless you, Alice.'[4]

Finally, don't take angry or abusive outbursts personally, these can be part of the illness or an expression of an unmet need; combine time with refreshments and informal conversations afterwards. And *keep your sense of humour*!

CONCLUSION

The spiritual needs of the frail older person can be the means to transcend circumstances and a support in times of loss, offering continuity, validation, personal dignity and a sense of worth, plus unconditional love. Maintaining spiritual life provides an opportunity to be able to express feelings, to forgive and be forgiven, to love and be loved, to be respected and not patronised, to rejoice in remaining skills, to be thankful, to have something to look forward to, to be listened to, and have time to think, retain faith and go on learning, to prepare for death, and to feel hope, beauty, belonging and expression of feeling.[5]

The person with dementia should have opportunities as a spiritual being to find meaning and purpose in the events of their life, to the extent of their capabilities.

We need to help them all we can.

ACTIVITY

Spend some time thinking of a mission statement for your church community in relation to providing support for older people with dementia, and their carers. Then, think of a short, meaningful Christian message that could be creatively communicated with Scripture and music. You might find these props useful to stimulate imagination: torch, blindfold, candle, map, bowl of water with sponge, packet of seeds.

REFLECTION

Quality of Life
Someone who listens
Someone to talk with
Kindness and understanding
Someone to laugh with
'Me' to see 'me' a lot
I like to be liked
I like to please
I like to know what pleases you
So that I can pass it on to someone else
Doing things, loving people
Letting them know you are thinking of them,
I like to see the light come into their face because I have said
something that really makes them happy,
… because I had so much unhappiness as a child
It is not so much about what people do but about relationship

Edith Brooking

Reflect on relationship, and the role it plays in your life; your relationship with God, and with other people.

How has what you have learned in this book affected you?

How has the insight into dementia given you an insight into what it means to be a human being, loved and valued by God?

PRAYER

Almighty Creator God, who made the universe, and everything in it; who created the stars but knows when a sparrow falls to the ground; how awesome You are, how great, how magnificent. Thank You that You invite us into relationship with You, through Your Son Jesus Christ, and His atoning work for us on the cross. Thank You that this is all by grace – Your free, undeserved favour – and not by works, and that we, as individuals, whether we are sick or well, are accepted and loved forever, in Christ our Saviour. Amen.

RESOURCES

T. Adams and J. Manthorpe (eds), *Dementia Care* (London: Arnold, 2003).

K. Albans, 'Looking at spirituality to enhance client wellbeing', *Nursing & Residential Care,* Vol. 5:5, 2003.

K. Allan, *Communication and Consultation: Exploring ways for staff to involve people with dementia in developing services* (Joseph Rowntree Foundation, 2001).

V. Bedwell, *God is With Us – some notes on services for the mentally frail* (booklet, 2005).

J. Burton-Jones and R. Hurtley, *Find the Right Care Home* (Age Concern England, 2008).

Christian Council on Ageing: *Is Anyone There? Guidelines for Worship and Prayer.*

P. Coleman, 'Is Religion the Friend of Ageing?', *Generations Review,* Vol. 14:4, 2004, pp.4–8.

Michael Collyer, Church Army: 'Discovering Faith in Later Life' series.

C. Crosskey, 'Older People, Faith and Dementia', Leveson Paper No. 7 (The Leveson Centre, 2004).

Dementia Group of the Christian Council on Ageing (*Dementia Newsletter* 33, 2009).

P. Garner, *Special Photograph Album,* third edition (2008).

M. Goldsmith *et al, Hearing the Voice of People with Dementia* (Dementia Development Centre, 1997).

G. Hammond and L. Moffitt, *Spiritual Care: Guidelines for care plans* (Christian Council on Ageing; Faith in Elderly People, Leeds, 2000).

Help the Aged, *Future Communities – Re-shaping our society for older people* (2009).

P. Higgins and R. Allen, *Lighting the Way* (SW London and St George's Mental NHS Trust, 2005).

P. Higgins and R. Allen, *Lighting the Way: Spiritual and religious care for those with dementia* (Solihull: The Leveson Centre, 2007).

L. Hobbs, 'Communication and Dementia', *Journal of Dementia Care*, Vol. 17:2, April 2009.

K. Howse, 'Religion and Spirituality in Later Life' *Generations Review*, Vol. 14:4, 2004, pp. 16-19.

R. Hurtley and J. Wenborn, *The Successful Activity Co-ordinator* (Age Concern England, 2005).

M. Johnson, 'Committed to the Asylum', Leveson Paper No. 3 (Solihull: The Leveson Centre, 2001).

Tom Kitwood on Dementia - a reader and critical commentary, edited by Clive Baldwin and Andrea Capstick, (Open University Press, 2007).

Supportive Care for the Person with Dementia, editors Julian C. Hughes, Mark Lloyd-Williams and Greg Sachs (Oxford University Press, 2010).

R. Lawrence, 'Aspects of spirituality in dementia care', *Dementia*, Vol. 2, No. 3, 2003, pp. 393-402.

Leveson Paper No. 6, 'Dementia: improving quality of life' (Leveson Centre seminar, 2003).

E. MacKinlay, *Spiritual Growth and Care in the Fourth Age of Life* (London: Jessica Kingsley Publishers, 2006).

R. Merchant, 'Spirituality, the new religion', *Generations Review*, Vol. 14:4, 2004, pp. 25-6.

J. Murphy, C. Gray and S. Cox, *Communication and Dementia* (Joseph Rowntree Foundation, 2007).

SCOP, Spiritual Care for Older People (Board for Social Responsibility, Diocese of Oxford, 2006).

CONTACTS

Alzheimer's Society

Provides information and local support to help people with dementia and their carers cope with the day-to-day realities of dementia. It funds research and campaigns on issues connected with dementia.

Devon House, 58 St Katherine's Way, London E1W 1JX
Tel: 020 7423 3500
Helpline: 0845 300 0336
 www.alzheimers.org.uk

Carers UK

Improves carers' lives through research, information, provision of services and campaigning.

20-25 Glasshouse Yard, London EC1A 4JT
Tel: 020 7490 8818
Helpline: 0808 808 7777
www.carersuk.org

Counsel and Care

Provides advice, information and financial support for those looking for the best care and support for older people. Influences national policies on services and funding.

Twyman House, 16 Bonny Street, London NW1 9PG
Tel: 020 7241 8555
Helpline: 0845 300 7585
www.counselandcare.org.uk

Crossroads Association

Provides breaks for carers to meet their individual needs.
Branches in most parts of England and Wales.

10 Regent Place, Rugby, Warwickshire CV21 2PN
Tel. 0845 450 0350
www.crossroads.org.uk

Cruse Bereavement Care

Promotes the wellbeing of bereaved people, providing counselling
and support.

PO Box 800, Richmond, Surrey TW9 1RG
Tel: 020 8939 9530
Helpline: 0844 477 9400
www.crusebereavementcare.org.uk

Relatives and Residents Association

Supports older people finding or living in care homes, and their families
and friends.

24 The Ivories, 6-18 Northampton Street, London N1 2HY
Tel: 020 7359 8148
Helpline: 020 7359 8136
www.relres.org

Christian Council on Ageing

Aims to assist churches and individual Christians to respond to the
pastoral needs of older people.

3 Stuart Street, Derby DE1 2EQ
Tel: 0845 094 4161
www.ccoa.org.uk

USEFUL WEBSITES

The Outlook Trust: **www.outlook-trust.org.uk**

The Sheffield Centre Church Army's research unit: **ask@sheffield.org.uk**;
Tel: 0114 272 7451; Michael Collyer m.collyer@churcharmy.org.uk

Parche: **www.parche.org.uk**

The Leveson Centre: **www.leveson.org.uk**

SCIE (Social Care Institute for Excellence) Dementia Gateway:
www.scie.org.uk/publications/dementia/index.asp

Admiral Nurses: **www.fordementia.org.uk**

For information for those with relatives in care homes:
www.myhomelife.org.uk

APPENDIX 1

SCRIPTURES

ANXIETY
Matthew 6:25,27,34:
(Words of Jesus) 'Therefore I tell you, do not worry about your life, what you will eat or drink; or about your body, what you will wear. Is not life more important than food, and the body more important than clothes? ... Who of you by worrying can add a single hour to his life? ... Therefore do not worry about tomorrow, for tomorrow will worry about itself. Each day has enough trouble of its own.'

1 Peter 5:7:
Cast all your anxiety on him because he cares for you.

Proverbs 18:10:
 The name of the LORD is a strong tower;
 the righteous run to it and are safe.

Isaiah 66:13:
(The Lord says)
'As a mother comforts her child,
so will I comfort you;
and you will be comforted over Jerusalem.'

Isaiah 8:11–12:
The LORD spoke to me with his strong hand upon me, warning me not to follow the way of this people. He said:
'Do not call conspiracy
everything that these people call conspiracy;

do not fear what they fear,
and do not dread it.'

Hebrews 13:6:
So we say with confidence,
'The Lord is my helper; I will not be afraid.
What can man do to me?'

ANGER
Psalm 46:10:
'Be still, and know that I am God ...'

John 14:27:
(Words of Jesus) 'Peace I leave with you; my peace I give you.
I do not give to you as the world gives. Do not let your hearts be
troubled and do not be afraid.'

LONELINESS
Hebrews 13:5:
'Never will I leave you;
never will I forsake you.'

Psalm 13:1–2:
How long, O Lord? Will you forget me forever?
How long will you hide your face from me?
How long must I wrestle with my thoughts
and every day have sorrow in my heart?

Isaiah 49:15
'Can a mother forget the baby at her breast
and have no compassion on the child she has borne?
Though she may forget,
I will not forget you!'

Jeremiah 31:3
The LORD appeared to us in the past, saying:
'I have loved you with an everlasting love;
I have drawn you with loving-kindness.'

FRUSTRATION
Psalm 91:15:
'He will call upon me, and I will answer him;
I will be with him in trouble,
I will deliver him and honour him.'

Matthew 11:28:
(Words of Jesus) 'Come to me, all you who are weary and
burdened, and I will give you rest.'

TIREDNESS
Isaiah 40:28–31
Do you not know?
Have you not heard?
The LORD is the everlasting God,
the Creator of the ends of the earth.
He will not grow tired or weary,
and his understanding no-one can fathom.
He gives strength to the weary
and increases the power of the weak.
Even youths grow tired and weary,

and young men stumble and fall;
but those who hope in the LORD
will renew their strength.
They will soar on wings like eagles;
they will run and not grow weary,
they will walk and not be faint.

Isaiah 43:2
'When you pass through the waters,
I will be with you;
and when you pass through the rivers,
they will not sweep over you.
When you walk through the fire,
you will not be burned;
the flames will not set you ablaze.'

Matthew 11:28–29
(Words of Jesus) 'Come to me, all you who are weary and
burdened, and I will give you rest. Take my yoke upon you and
learn from me, for I am gentle and humble in heart, and you
will find rest for your souls.'

Psalm 29:11
The LORD gives strength to his people;
the LORD blesses his people with peace.

GUILT
Psalm 46:1
God is our refuge and strength,
an ever-present help in trouble.

LOSS/GRIEF

Matthew 5:4:
(Words of Jesus) 'Blessed are those who mourn,
for they will be comforted.'

Matthew 6:34:
(Words of Jesus) 'Therefore do not worry about tomorrow, for tomorrow will worry about itself. Each day has enough trouble of its own.'

Isaiah 49:13:
Shout for joy, O heavens;
rejoice, O earth;
burst into song, O mountains!
For the LORD comforts his people
and will have compassion on his afflicted ones.

Hebrews 13:8:
Jesus Christ is the same yesterday and today and forever.

Isaiah 30:19:
O people of Zion, who live in Jerusalem, you will weep no more. How gracious he will be when you cry for help! As soon as he hears, he will answer you.

1 Thessalonians 4:17–18
After that, we who are still alive and are left will be caught up together with them in the clouds to meet the Lord in the air. And so we will be with the Lord for ever. Therefore encourage each other with these words.

APPENDIX 2

RESTOR8 PRINCIPLES

1. **Restoring relationship** of a person to their former self and to others around them by building an image of a person through activities and roles which match the former lifestyle, individual preferences and current cognitive level of an individual through a range of therapeutic media using the biography to inform these with accurate ongoing assessment, thus providing a mutual and 'complete community'.
2. **Developing** an environment where novelty and new experiences gently challenge and stimulate individuals, probing for improved function; thus, ongoing learning experiences can take place.
3. **Activating:** ability-focused, meaningful activity, adapted to abilities, whether spontaneous or planned. Finding out the level of function and working within the capabilities of the individual providing as many opportunities for choice and involvement as possible.
4. **Communicating** an approach to activities in a way which includes an imaginative presentation … the potential of them to be appreciated by all involved, so that all can enjoy making the ordinary extraordinary, focusing on the 'little things that matter'. This will involve an intense understanding and effective communication skills.
5. **Enriching** the environment to maximise wellbeing; it should aim to be stable and peaceful and offer a range of targeted, meaningful activities and 'sensory enrichments' which foster interdependent, mutual social-supported living: access to animals, children, nature and the outdoors and the wider community where possible.

6. **Releasing** creativity within the relationships surrounding the person, which can be tapped for the mutual support and benefit of the person with dementia, through education and understanding.
7. **Empathising** by validation and support of the emotional experience of the world lived in by the person with dementia, and how it affects those in relationship with them.
8. **Connecting** with the wider community and preventing social isolation.

(R. Hurtley, RESTOR8 Principles, 2006)

APPENDIX 3

RELATIONSHIP-CENTRED CARE

Relationship-centred care is an approach which will enable older people, their relatives and care staff, whether receiving care at home or in a care setting, to experience home life in ways that generate and sustain their wellbeing and quality of life. Nolan's Six Senses Framework (M. Nolan *et al.* 'Beyond person centred care – a new vision for gerontological nursing', *International Journal of Older People Nursing*, No. 13, 2004, pp. 3a, 45–53) summarised below can help us to understand the positive consequences of achieving person-centred relationship activated care. Effective person-centred care is best achieved when relationships between and among all those involved are positive.

RELATIONSHIP-CENTRED CARE/THE SIX SENSES FRAMEWORK

1. A Sense of Security – to feel safe, and receive or deliver competent and sensitive care.
2. A Sense of Continuity – recognition of biography, using the past to make sense of the present, and help to plan for the future.
3. A Sense of Belonging – providing opportunities to form meaningful relationships or to feel part of a team.
4. A Sense of Purpose – providing opportunities to engage in purposeful activity, or to have a clear set of goals to aim for.
5. A Sense of Fulfilment – achieving meaningful or valued goals and feeling satisfied with one's efforts.
6. A Sense of Significance – to feel that you, and what you do, matters, and that you are valued as a person.

This supports the Resident Centred Care Home Standard™ developed for care homes by the author.

THE PRINCIPLES UNDERPINNING THE RCC-HOME STANDARD™

1. Resident-centred care is dependent on the development and maintenance of positive relationships across and between the resident, their close relatives/friends and staff, often referred to as the 'relationship triangle' (a triad of relationships as reflected in the Trinity in relationship).

2. Residents will judge their experience of life in a care home more positively if the home's owners, managers and staff are person-centred in attitude and behaviour towards them.

3. Relatives and other close carers visiting the resident will judge their own experiences more positively if managers and staff recognise the roles of relatives and close carers and respond with understanding.

4. Staff will judge their experience of working with older people as more satisfying and worthwhile, and be more person-centred in their work, if they feel valued by their employer and equipped to fulfil their caring roles in resident-focused ways.

5. The RCC-Home Standard™ is achievable in care home organisations where owners, managers and staff are committed to making it happen.

(Pat Duff, Rosemary Hurtley, 2005)

APPENDIX 4

PAL

A summary of the Pool Activity Levels, representing four levels of cognitive ability.[1]

PLANNED ACTIVITY LEVEL

When someone can work towards the completion of a task but will encounter difficulties with issues which arise regarding solving problems. Keep sentences short to communicate most effectively at this level. Carers needed to help solve problems.

EXPLORATORY ACTIVITY LEVEL

The person can carry out familiar tasks in familiar surroundings. Activities should be broken into small chunks. Directions given should be simple – memory aids, lists. Employ a spontaneous and creative approach.

SENSORY ACTIVITY LEVEL

The person will be more concerned with feeling/sensation than thoughts/ideas regarding carrying out activities. At this level, someone can be guided to do simple, one-step tasks. Directions must emphasise key words; demonstrate required action.

REFLEX ACTIVITY LEVEL

The person may not be aware of their body or environment. Use direct stimulation to enter their world. In communication, language forms only a minor part. Use facial expression and reassuring voice for any word or single command.

NOTES

INTRODUCTION
1. Unknown source.

CHAPTER 1
1. Data from Help the Aged, *Future Communities – Re-shaping our society for older people* (2009).
2. Adapted from Rosemary Hurtley, *Provision of Activities in a Care Setting* (York: Network Training Publishing, 2006).
3. Alzheimer's Fact Sheet 401, *What is Alzheimer's Disease?* (Alzheimer's Society, 2000).
4. Alzheimers Society Factsheet 402
5. Adapted from G. Stokes, F. Goudie (eds), *Working with Dementia* (Bicester: Winslow Press, 1990).
6. Adapted from C. Wells, 'Pseudodementia', *American Journal of Psychiatry*, 136:7, 1979, pp. 895–900.
7. Ref: www.thehealthguide.org.

CHAPTER 2
1. National Association for Providers of Activities for Older People (NAPA): Tutor's manual for the City and Guilds 6977 certificate in providing therapeutic activities for older people. Written by Rosemary Hurtley.
2. G. Stokes and F. Goudie, *Working with Dementia* (Bicester: Winslow Press, 1990).
3. Material sourced from Alzheimer's Society, 2009.
4. Adapted from K. Allen, *Communication and Consultation – Exploring ways for staff to involve people with dementia in developing services* (Joseph Rowntree Foundation, 2001).
5. J. Powell, 'Care to Communicate – helping the older person with dementia', Journal of Dementia Care, 2000.
6. Richard Cheston and Elizabeth Bartlett, 'Counselling people with dementia' in T. Adams and J. Manthorpe (eds), *Dementia Care* (London: Arnold, 2003).
7. Adapted from Alzheimer's Society Fact Sheet 523.

8. Crossroads is Britain's leading provider of support for carers and people they support.
9. Julia Burton-Jones and Rosemary Hurtley, *Find the Right Care Home* (Age Concern England, 2008).
10. Ibid.

CHAPTER 3
1. A summary from Sue Benson (ed.), *New Culture and Old Culture of Dementia Care* (London: Hawker Publications, 1995).
2. *At Least Five a Week: evidence of the importance of physical activity and its relationship to health* (Department of Health, 2004: www.dh.gov.uk).
3. Naomi Feil, *Validation: The Feil Method* (Cleveland, Ohio: Edward Feil Productions, 2003).
4. T. Kitwood, *Dementia Reconsidered* (Buckingham: Open University Press, 1997).

CHAPTER 4
1. T. Kitwood, *Dementia Reconsidered* (Buckingham: Open University Press, 1997).
2. *Nourishing the Inner Being* – Training Video produced by MHA Care Group 2002.
3. E. Bruce, 'Looking after the wellbeing: a tool for evaluation', *Journal of Dementia Care*, Nov.-Dec. 25-27, 2002.

CHAPTER 5
1. Adapted from: Jackie Pool, *The Pool Activity Level Instrument for Occupational Profiling* (London: Jessica Kingsley Publishers, 2008). Third edition.
2. Alzheimer's Society Fact Sheet 429.
3. R. Hurtley and J. Wenborn, *The Successful Activity Co-ordinator* (Age Concern England, 2005).
4. T. Kitwood, *Dementia Reconsidered* (Buckingham: Open University, 1997).

CHAPTER 6

1. Much of the material in this chapter is from Julia Burton-Jones and Rosemary Hurtley, *Find the Right Care Home* (Age Concern England, 2008).
2. This data first appeared in Julia Burton-Jones and Rosemary Hurtley, *Find the Right Care Home*.
3. See R. Hurtley, 'What to look for in a care home', *Care Select,* Winter 2008–Spring 2009
4. The *Training Manual for Care Homes* (for the Holisitic Care Of Older People) by Gaynor Hammond is available through Faith in Elderly People, Leeds.
5. T. Adams and J. Manthorpe (eds), *Dementia Care* (London: Arnold, 2003).

CHAPTER 7

1. E. Shamy, *More than body, brain and breath: A guide to spiritual care of people with Alzheimer's disease* (New Zealand: ColCom Press, 1997).
2. R. Hurtley and J. Wenborn, *The Successful Activity Co-ordinator* (Age Concern England, 2005); E. MacKinlay, *Spiritual Growth and Care in the Fourth Age of Life* (London: Jessica Kingsley Publishers, 2006).
3. E. MacKinlay, *Spiritual Growth and Care in the Fourth Age of Life* (London: Jessica Kingsley Publishers, 2006).
4. Adapted from Rev Donald Bell, *Services in Homes* (Christian Council on Ageing, 1993).
5. Alison Froggatt, 'Tuning into Spiritual Needs', *Journal of Dementia Care,* Vol. 2, Issue 2, 1994, pp. 12–13; Jeff Garland and Christina Garland, 'A Matter of Time', *Journal of Dementia Care,* Vol. 6, Issue 4, 1998 pp. 22–23; E. MacKinlay, *Spiritual Growth and Care in the Fourth Age of Life* (London: Jessica Kingsley Publishers, 2006).

APPENDIX 4

1. Adapted from: Jackie Pool, *The Pool Activity Level Instrument for Occupational Profiling* (London: Jessica Kingsley Publishers, 2008). Third edition.

NATIONAL DISTRIBUTORS

UK: (and countries not listed below)

CWR, Waverley Abbey House, Waverley Lane, Farnham, Surrey GU9 8EP.
Tel: (01252) 784700 Outside UK (44) 1252 784700 Email: mail@cwr.org.uk

AUSTRALIA: KI Entertainment, Unit 21 317-321 Woodpark Road, Smithfield,
New South Wales 2164.
Tel: 1 800 850 777 Fax: 02 9604 3699 Email: sales@kientertainment.com.au

CANADA: David C Cook Distribution Canada, PO Box 98, 55 Woodslee Avenue,
Paris, Ontario N3L 3E5.
Tel: 1800 263 2664 Email: swansons@cook.ca

GHANA: Challenge Enterprises of Ghana, PO Box 5723, Accra.
Tel: (021) 222437/223249 Fax: (021) 226227 Email: ceg@africaonline.com.gh

HONG KONG: Cross Communications Ltd, 1/F, 562A Nathan Road, Kowloon.
Tel: 2780 1188 Fax: 2770 6229 Email: cross@crosshk.com

INDIA: Crystal Communications, 10-3-18/4/1, East Marredpalli, Secunderabad
– 500026, Andhra Pradesh.
Tel/Fax: (040) 27737145 Email: crystal_edwj@rediffmail.com

KENYA: Keswick Books and Gifts Ltd, PO Box 10242-00400, Nairobi.
Tel: (254) 20 312639/3870125 Email: keswick@swiftkenya.com

MALAYSIA: Canaanland, No. 25 Jalan PJU 1A/41B, NZX Commercial Centre, Ara Jaya,
47301 Petaling Jaya, Selangor.
Tel: (03) 7885 0540/1/2 Fax: (03) 7885 0545 Email: info@canaanland.com.my

Salvation Book Centre (M) Sdn Bhd, 23 Jalan SS 2/64, 47300 Petaling Jaya, Selangor.
Tel: (03) 78766411/78766797 Fax: (03) 78757066/78756360
Email: info@salvationbookcentre.com

NEW ZEALAND: KI Entertainment, Unit 21 317-321 Woodpark Road, Smithfield,
New South Wales 2164, Australia.
Tel: 0 800 850 777 Fax: +612 9604 3699 Email: sales@kientertainment.com.au

NIGERIA: FBFM, Helen Baugh House, 96 St Finbarr's College Road, Akoka, Lagos.
Tel: (01) 7747429/4700218/825775/827264 Email: fbfm@hyperia.com

PHILIPPINES: OMF Literature Inc, 776 Boni Avenue, Mandaluyong City.
Tel: (02) 531 2183 Fax: (02) 531 1960 Email: gloadlaon@omflit.com

SINGAPORE: Alby Commercial Enterprises Pte Ltd, 95 Kallang Avenue #04-00,
AIS Industrial Building, 339420.
Tel: (65) 629 27238 Fax: (65) 629 27235 Email: marketing@alby.com.sg

SOUTH AFRICA: Struik Christian Books, 80 MacKenzie Street, PO Box 1144,
Cape Town 8000.
Tel: (021) 462 4360 Fax: (021) 461 3612 Email: info@struikchristianmedia.co.za

SRI LANKA: Christombu Publications (Pvt) Ltd, Bartleet House, 65 Braybrooke
Place, Colombo 2.
Tel: (9411) 2421073/2447665 Email: dhanad@bartleet.com

USA: David C Cook Distribution Canada, PO Box 98, 55 Woodslee Avenue, Paris,
Ontario N3L 3E5, Canada. Tel: 1800 263 2664 Email: swansons@cook.ca

**CWR is a Registered Charity - Number 294387. CWR is a Limited
Company registered in England - Registration Number 1990308**

Day and Residential Courses
Counselling Training
Leadership Development
Biblical Study Courses
Regional Seminars
Ministry to Women
Daily Devotionals
Books and DVDs
Conference Centre

Trusted all Over the World

CWR HAS GAINED A WORLDWIDE
reputation as a centre of excellence for
Bible-based training and resources. From
our headquarters at Waverley Abbey House,
Farnham, England, we have been serving
God's people for over 40 years with a vision
to help apply God's Word to everyday life
and relationships. The daily devotional *Every
Day with Jesus* is read by nearly a million
readers an issue in more than 150 countries,
and our unique courses in biblical studies
and pastoral care are respected all over the
world. Waverley Abbey House provides a
conference centre in a tranquil setting.

For free brochures on our seminars and
courses, conference facilities, or a catalogue
of CWR resources, please contact us at the
following address:
CWR, Waverley Abbey House, Waverley Lane,
Farnham, Surrey GU9 8EP, UK

Telephone: **+44 (0)1252 784700**
Email: **mail@cwr.org.uk**
Website: **www.cwr.org.uk**

CWR Applying God's Word
to everyday life and relationships

More insights from our wealth of experience

The *Waverley Abbey Insight Series* brings together biblical understanding and practical advice to offer clear insight, teaching and help on a range of issues.

 Insight into Addiction – Find out how addictions take hold and how to destroy their power at the roots, never to rise again.
ISBN: 978-1-85345-505-6

 Insight into Anger – Understand the deep roots of inappropriate anger, and overcome resentment, rage and bitterness.
ISBN: 978-1-85345-437-0

 Insight into Anxiety – Discover just what anxiety is, who is at risk of it and how to help those who suffer from it.
ISBN: 978-1-85345-436-3

 Insight into Assertiveness – Break with people-pleasing and build healthy relationships.
ISBN: 978-1-85345-539-1

 Insight into Bereavement – Work through the grieving process when a loved one dies, we experience divorce or the loss of a job etc.
ISBN: 978-1-85345-385-4

 Insight into Depression – Start to make sense of how you feel, and find hope that change is possible.
ISBN: 978-1-85345-538-4

 Insight into Eating Disorders – Discover the root causes of eating disorders and deal effectively with denial and self-destruction.
ISBN: 978-1-85345-410-3

 Insight into Forgiveness – Find freedom from the past through the power to forgive.
ISBN: 978-1-85345-491-2

 Insight into Perfectionism – Stop striving and live freely in God's accepting presence.
ISBN: 978-1-85345-506-3

 Insight into Self-esteem – Cultivate healthy self-esteem by deepening your relationship with God.
ISBN: 978-1-85345-409-7

 Insight into Stress – Recognise stress and its causes, and learn what you can do about it.
ISBN: 978-1-85345-384-7

£8.99 each